Basic Mathematics

Basic Mathematics

VOLUME ONE OF THE

Mathematics for Management Series

By

CLIFFORD H. SPRINGER

ROBERT E. HERLIHY

ROBERT I. BEGGS

Consultants, General Electric Company

1965

RICHARD D. IRWIN, INC.

HOMEWOOD, ILLINOIS

First Printing, August, 1965
Second Printing, March, 1966
Third Printing, October, 1966

Foreword

In recognition of the growing need for management to develop greater awareness of the contribution modern mathematical techniques can make to the decision-making process, our Company has had under development for several years now a "Mathematics for Management" Course. This book is one of a set of four being prepared specifically for this purpose. The remaining three volumes cover advanced methods and models, statistical inference, and probabilistic models.

This material has been developed under the auspices of our Comptroller's organization as a part of General Electric Company's overall formal training efforts to both develop potential managers and to enhance awareness of current management in all areas of the business. Individuals in other functional areas such as Engineering, Manufacturing and Marketing have as a result participated in this effort.

Our specific objective has been to develop awareness and understanding of mathematical applications to business situations without requiring the individual to become a technician or practitioner. Based on the experience of over 2,000 people who have participated in the Course in General Electric Company to date, these texts are accomplishing this purpose and thus provide the necessary communications link between management and the technician, which is so vital if the full benefits of rapidly developing scientific business methods are to be realized.

G. L. PHILLIPPE
CHAIRMAN OF THE BOARD
GENERAL ELECTRIC COMPANY

Preface

Most of us are aware that mathematics is playing an expanding role in the management decision-making process. Decisions that a short while ago were made by the "seat of the pants" are being made in the light of new knowledge gained through relatively new applications of mathematical and statistical concepts. As this trend toward more scientific decision-making continues, it is clear that those with an understanding of mathematics will have a marked advantage over those lacking such knowledge.

But what are the relevant aspects of mathematics? As the applications of mathematics to business problems increase in number and complexity, it becomes more difficult for the student of business to answer this question. Will linear programing become the keystone in the mathematics of business management? Or will it be Bayesian statistics, decision theory, or what?

The fact is that these and other powerful tools will increase in importance. But from the point of view of the business manager the most significant impact lies not in the elaborate analytical technique but in something simple by comparison and more subtle and penetrating in effect. It boils down to this: mathematics will help him examine, clarify and improve the logic in his decision-making.

To avail himself of these most important benefits, the business man need not attempt to approach the mathematical acumen, insight, or manipulative skills of the mathematician. Detailed knowledge of the mechanical aspects of elaborate but mystifying techniques is likewise of little value. What is required, and what we hope the Mathematics for Management Series will help accomplish, is to increase the student's knowledge and understanding of the *uses* of mathematics.

The Mathematics for Management Series is divided into four separate texts, the first of which is entitled *Basic Mathematics*. The remaining titles in sequential order are *Advanced Methods and Models*, *Statistical Inference*, and *Probabilistic Models*.

From an overall point of view the first two texts deal primarily with the kind of mathematics used to analyze or describe situations which are *determinate,* i.e., where questions of risk or uncertainty are not raised. In many real problems, this leads to good results—in fact, this view was essentially the only one seen in all of science until recent times. Even today this view is characteristic of many disciplines.

For many purposes, situations must be viewed as comprised in part of random effects which introduce uncertainty into some or all measurements. The last two texts are devoted to methods pertinent to this so-called *stochastic* view.

The first and third texts are similar in that they emphasize mathematical concepts associated with discovering inner relationships, i.e., those relationships in a problem situation that are not superficially revealed. In short these two sections are devoted primarily to the mathematics of *analysis.*

The second and fourth texts, in contrast, are devoted more to the use of mathematics to show how combinations of detailed effects act to produce overall system characteristics. In other words, the emphasis here is on building mathematical models which *synthesize* system behavior.

In addition to its relationship to other sections of the course as described above, *Basic Mathematics* must provide the foundation from which the ideas, principles, and methods used in later texts can be developed. To accomplish this, a broad range of mathematical topics must be considered. These include algebra (with aspects of analytic geometry), descriptive statistics, calculus, matrices, and set theory. The material is covered rapidly with emphasis on fundamentals and uses. The objective is to develop an appreciation of the uses of mathematics and the ability to read about mathematics and communicate with the technical practitioner about material beyond one's own ability to execute. To use an analogy, one need not have the ability to compose music or score it for a symphony orchestra to appreciate the world's great music. Neither must the business man be a mathematical virtuoso to understand and utilize the world's great mathematical ideas to improve his own decision-making, or to make effective use of mathematics within his organization.

Much of the material in *Basic Mathematics* will be a review of material covered in prior mathematics courses. In the case of the last two chapters on matrices and sets this may not be the case since these are elements of more modern mathematical thought. To the extent that the material is a review, it may serve to recall to accessibility a greater depth of materials than can be covered in the text. Those lacking depth in previous mathematical training may require a little more faith and patience, at least initially; but they need not feel too seriously hampered, for most of those with better mathematical backgrounds took courses directed primarily at the physical sciences. These courses are typically so far removed from the business environment that a triumph of reasoning would be required to relate them to problems having a business setting.

Two further points regarding *Basic Mathematics.* Some topics are introduced that, of necessity, relate directly to topics of more practical importance in later texts. This imposes certain limitations on the "environmental enrichment" or realism that can accompany the exposition of these topics. For instance, there is a strong urge to draw conclusions from a statistical description of a set of data. This urge will not be satisfied until the elements of drawing valid inferences are considered in *Statistical Inference.*

The final point: While mathematics is in many respects a language of its own, it is not a language that is easily read by the non-mathematician. We have avoided in this text the stilted style of the mathematical language to a large extent. Instead we favor simple, vernacular English which we feel will be much more comfortable for most of our readers.

New York
July, 1965

C. H. Springer
R. E. Herlihy
R. I. Beggs

Table of Contents

CHAPTER 1

The Language of Mathematics

1. About Mathematics

1.1 WHAT IS MATHEMATICS?

In 1962, a noted educator proposed changes to the U.S. school
system which would compel each high school graduate to be able to
read and write two foreign languages: English and Mathematics.
His tongue may have been in his cheek, even though there is much
evidence to support his implication, but he at least showed rare
perceptiveness in defining mathematics as a *language*. Louis Kattsoff, in his 1948 book, *A Philosophy of Mathematics,* after an entire
chapter devoted to the discussion of eleven significantly different
definitions of mathematics, writes that "it is almost possible to say
that mathematics is a language and that its elements (groups of
symbols) are the 'words' of the language . . . such a point of view
explains the different definitions of mathematics and the reason
it has taken us so long to see the nature of mathematics."[1] Way
back in 1932 a scholarly book called *A Linguistic Analysis of Mathematics* was published, but it failed to become popular with either
linguists or mathematicians.

But now the situation is different. Books and articles are appearing regularly which clarify many mathematical ideas for the reader
by appealing to his knowledge of another language. Although Modern Algebra may never be taught in the School of Modern Languages of a university, this could certainly be more easily defended
today than its placement in, say, the School of Engineering.

Historically, mathematics developed along several different lines,
chief among them being its development as (1) a *science of num-*

---

[1] Reprinted by permission from *A Philosophy of Mathematics* by Louis O. Kattsoff,
copyright 1948 by The Iowa State University Press, Ames, Iowa.

ber and (2) as a *science of space*. By reason of this history, beginners in mathematics have been taught according to one or both of these traditional patterns, and it is only in recent years that the so-called *modern* view of the subject has begun to influence our educational processes. A brief review of mathematics as both the science of number and the science of space is in order, because understanding the modern notion of mathematics as a language is easier when two already familiar instances of the use of the language are compared.

1.2   A SCIENCE OF NUMBER

Although we can only speculate upon the origins of numbers, it is easy enough to imagine how they *might* have been invented. Perhaps the owner of a flock of sheep, suspicious of his shepherd's integrity, began one day to wonder whether the "many" sheep which came home at dusk were "less" than the "many" which he watched depart at dawn. Searching for a way to protect his assets by comparing the same flock at two different times, the owner hit upon a scheme of standing at the gate in the morning and breaking off a small piece of twig as each animal filed by. Taking them out of the pouch one-by-one at night to reverse the process served him very well. Later on, someone using this method began to render small grunts of satisfaction as each bit of twig was discarded, thus beginning the centuries-long development of the ritual chant we call *counting*. The grunts became a version of our "one, two, three, . . ." and corresponded to what was seen in the pile of sticks: $|$, $|$ $|$, $|$ $|$ $|$, ... Soon, saying the final grunt achieved in the counting process was recognized as an excellent way to communicate the "howmanyness" of a collection of objects to another similarly skilled. Also, a picture of the final state of the pile of sticks was a splendid symbol for recording that characteristic of a set of objects which is now called *number*.

Once counting was established, people began to note interesting relationships. When two families joined for a common meal, the host might notice that "when my two children are placed by my guest's three children, there are five children." This is merely a straightforward observation of a *fact*, and not especially important except for planning that particular meal. But seeing repetitions of this combination, and noting that each time he obtained the same result, the host might take the first step of generalization, and conclude, "if one puts two children with three children, there will be five children." This remark was much different, being truly scientific, for it *predicted the result of an unperformed experiment.*

The next step in the generalization process occurred when someone noted that what he had observed as true about children was *also* true about sticks, dogs, spears, etc., and thus was led to venture that "if two things are put with three things, there will be five things." Since the truth of this statement seems to have absolutely nothing to do with the nature of the objects involved, it must therefore be a truth concerning the *numbers* two, three, and five. The collection of all such statements, in fact, constitutes a science, not of real objects, but of concepts called "numbers." This science of numbers is known as "Arithmetic."

The last stage of generalization is vital, but surely the most subtle. A number such as "three" is now considered as an entity itself, rather than as one property of a collection of objects. This attitude toward numbers is exemplified when, on the golf course, a twosome and a threesome join to make a fivesome. Note that this action joins two objects (one twosome and one threesome) to make a single new object (one fivesome), which is a distinctly *different* operation than joining two objects with three objects to yield five objects. (This latter operation is familiar addition, but the former is known in the modern Theory of Sets as *union.*) At first glance, this last step in generalizing may appear trivial, but it is, in fact, the most important, because it eliminates the necessity for making physical experiments, by substituting logical reasoning (i.e., mental experiments) for them. Under such circumstances, it is possible to invent an assortment of (imaginary) objects which possess whatever (imaginary) properties one desires, and which obey whatever (imaginary) rules one chooses, then to perform (imaginary) mental experiments with them and observe the (imaginary) results. But this is precisely what mathematicians do, namely, mathematics.

If this sounds like something from *Alice in Wonderland,* it is because the structure of mathematics has no physical existence; it is pure abstraction. A similar but perhaps more familiar abstract process is the game of Bridge. This also involves certain objects (cards) that possess properties (the ace of trumps is high, etc.); and, of course, the game has its rules. Before playing a card, it is customary to first conduct a mental experiment. This experiment is purely imaginary. It is not confused with the actual playing of a card nor do the cards assume physical meaning during the thought process (the Queen of Hearts is no more than a symbol). So it is with mathematics. The mathematician treats his objects (symbols) like the deck of cards. He manipulates them according to rules without encumbering the thought process by attaching concrete meaning to them. The difference between the game of Bridge and the applied science of Mathematics, however, lies in the fact that the mathematician attempts to play his game using rules that exist in a real situation. Before and after the game (but not during) he wants to be able to show a correspondence between his imaginary objects and concrete physical counterparts.

1.3 A SCIENCE OF SPACE

It could be true that the only ancients who possessed simultaneously (a) curiosity, (b) idle time, and (c) a handy set of sticks in various lengths, were the early-model mathematicians, who, we can suppose, made their meagre livings sitting all day at the ranchers' gates with their pouches of twigs, thus allowing the ranchers to enjoy frivolities at night and still sleep late the next morning. At any rate, one of them one day might have arranged a dozen bits of twig, all of the same length, into a triangular pattern with three, four, and five bits on a side and noted the perpendicularity of the two sides of the right triangle. He and his friends had long been using their unit-length sticks to talk about distances ("it's eleven rods from the cave to the river") and, in fact, had developed a rather refined *science of measure* based on the existing science of number.

But this was something different, it seemed. Perhaps the discoverer of this magic property we now call "perpendicularity" ascribed it to the very set of twelve sticks used in the original experiment. How disappointed he must have been when it was discovered that the trick also worked with *other* mathematicians' sticks, too. What was at first a private fact became a scientific law, which after many more experiments was found to be true regardless of the (common) length of the sticks, their diameter, or even their material composition. Taking a clue from earlier experiences, it was suggested that the mysterious right angle was a property of the *numbers* three, four, and five, but this seemed to lead nowhere.

Eventually, of course, the right angle came to have a special identity all its own, and was itself recognized as just one property of a right triangle. Gradually this line of approach led to an applied *science of space,* a science which proved of tremendous practical value to a budding civilization.

But there remained one further step to be taken, that of formulating the science in such terms that pure logic and the power of reason would obviate completely the necessity for further physical experiments. Thus geometry was to become an *abstract* science rather than a physical one.

The Greeks took this last step in generalizing by introducing the concepts of point, line, angle, etc., and certain axioms (rules) about them (e.g., "through any two points may be drawn one and only one line"). They defined these concepts and axioms as pure abstractions, i.e., without physical existence. For instance, they recognized that two dabs of black ink on a piece of paper with a streak of ink between them were not the same thing as their imaginary definitions of points and lines. They were able to demonstrate properties of this set of (imaginary) objects by force of pure reason alone. This so-called "axiomatization" of the science of space preceded by two millenia the similar treatment of the science of number. For this, the Greeks, especially Euclid and his friends, have been cursed by generation after generation of high school sophomores who, largely as a result of unquestioned tradition, have been confronted with a more-or-less rigorous axiomatic approach to geometry, because "it's good for them." It is (or would be) if only the student knew *what* he was studying and *why*.

How many millions of geometry students have suffered through the proof of an "obvious" theorem, without ever recognizing the difference between an *obvious physical* theorem ("if all sides of a cardboard triangle are made equal in length, the angles will be found to measure equal") and the *nonobvious* (but demonstrable) *abstract* theorem which corresponds to it. The former is *supportable* but not *provable:* as you make more and more cardboard equilateral triangles, you will become more and more convinced of the equiangularity of such objects. The latter is completely different: the abstract theorem must either be

Assumed true or false (i.e., be one of the invented axioms),
Or it must be logically derivable from the axioms,
Or it must be logically false.

Abstract theorems *are* provable, and the processes that mathematicians use for such purposes parallel very closely the *thought* processes which humans use to reason about the world. As a matter of fact, any branch of mathematics could be described as just a system for expressing and/or communicating human thought. And that is precisely the dictionary definition of the word *language!*

2.   Mathematical Symbols

2.1   MATHEMATICS AS A LANGUAGE

While the dictionary definition of the word *language* does not distinguish between the spoken and written forms, most people think of mathematics as being mostly written—even though no one has yet succeeded in writing anything which cannot be read aloud. If the man-in-the-street were handed two books, one an English grammar and the other a book on mathematics, he would probably have no difficulty deciding which book was mathematical. Why is this so? If the books were both written in an unfamiliar language, he might not be certain which was the math book, after all. Actually, any book is simply a collection of printed marks arranged on paper as a record of ideas or thoughts, and unless one's vocabulary includes some of these marks he would be unable to decipher the contents.

For most popular languages, dictionaries are available which list, in lexicographical order, some words which form the partial vocabulary of the language. These words are *symbols* (themselves formed from a small collection of other symbols called an "alphabet") which when used as spoken sound or written mark serve to stand for some object or some idea. In addition, the dictionary gives for each word some definitions, which are simply other words or groups of words which are synonymous with the original word in various contexts. Subject to certain rules, these words may be put together in groups as expressions or phrases or sentences when more elaborate thoughts are to be expressed. The rules for putting words together constitute what is called "syntax." The entire science which concerns not only syntax but other rules regarding punctuation, word classifications, inflections, etc., is known as "grammar."

Thus a language amounts to a vocabulary of symbols and rules for using those symbols. In a natural language such as English, the symbols are words and the rules are grammar. In mathematics, some of the symbols (like 1, 2, 5, π, e, $\sqrt{}$, point, line, $+$, $\div$, etc.) have developed organically over long periods of time and are widely recognized, while others are newly invented as needed. Some of the rules which govern certain mathematical vocabularies are traditional in character, like the axioms of Arithmetic or Euclidean Geometry . . . others are purposefully invented.

2.2 CONSTANTS

The Cross, Uncle Sam, and the olive branch are symbols. But the word "symbol" applies as well to any written or printed mark used as a visible indication of something unseen. The letter "a" is such a symbol. If the letter "a" were standing alone, one would have some difficulty identifying just what it signified except, perhaps, that it represented the first letter of the alphabet. It takes on different meanings, however, depending on other letter symbols found near it, as in the symbols "far" and "fair." Likewise the symbol "fair" depends on other word symbols close at hand, as in expressions like "fair weather," "Play fair!" "county fair," etc. The same applies to symbols like "6." It signifies sixty in the symbol "68" and six hundred in the symbol "3,624."

In the vocabulary of English there are several kinds of words, such as noun, verb, adjective, and so on. In the mathematical language one finds similar distinctions. For example, English grammarians call symbols *proper nouns* when they serve in a given context as the *name* of a specific thing. The *proper nouns* of the mathematical language are called constants. The symbol "GE," a proper noun, stands for the General Electric Company. The symbol "8," a constant, stands for the eighth number in the sequence which begins "one, two, three." A constant which names a number is called a *numeral*, so the symbol "8" is also a numeral.

Note the distinction between the words "number" and "numeral." A numeral is a symbol used to stand for a number. A number, on the other hand, is an abstract idea, or concept. Arithmetic is a practical science about *numbers*, but to read about arithmetic it is first necessary to learn the *numerals*. It is interesting to note that children already know a good deal about numbers long before they can read numerals. For example, the child in the candy store with five pennies knows he can get "two of these and three of those," even though he cannot read the written statement "2 + 3 = 5." This is a statement using symbols, which says that "2 + 3" is another name for whatever the symbol "5" stands for. When the child goes to school and learns that 2 + 3 = 5, he has simply learned to read and write about an arithmetic problem he already solved in the candy store. As his elementary schooling continues, he will discover many more ways in which numerals can be arranged to write facts about numbers. In many of these facts, of course, will lie answers to arithmetic problems he has not yet encountered.

A lot of people nowadays feel that such distinctions as these are just "fine points" because they learned Arithmetic very well thank you without getting so "technical." Well, that's all right if you plan to study only Arithmetic—but if you plan to go further in mathematics, then it is better to do it right. Educators are finding out that people can learn mathematics faster and better if they *begin* by taking pains to emphasize the *abstract* nature of the subject. In this way, they are able to apply their knowledge of *pure* mathematics to both the learning and the using of several different branches of *applied* mathematics. As a consequence, we might occasionally see familiar symbols being used in unfamiliar ways.

To illustrate, let us assume one sees a statement like "3 + 6 = 2." He may automatically assume that the symbols name *numbers,* in which case the statement appears to be just bad arithmetic. Actually, these are familiar symbols which are being used in a convenient but different way. When it boils down to a question of who is in charge, the symbols or the mathematician, the mathematician answers "me!" and goes on about his business. In this case, the mathematician may have found it convenient to assign a numeral to name each day of the week: 1 = Sunday, 2 = Monday, and so on. If this were the case, then it can be verified that 3 + 6 = 2, i.e., that the sixth day after a Tuesday is a Monday. (The careful person would also ask whether 6 + 3 = 3 + 6, i.e., is the third day after Friday also a Monday?)

Let us pause here long enough to exert our power over symbols by inventing one of our own. We will see shortly that this will serve a useful purpose.

In the balance of this text, exercises will be inserted within the body of the text material. The reason for this is that mathematics, like hunting and fishing, is not much of a spectator sport. A certain amount of contact is necessary to find out what it's all about. Unlike most sports, however, the contact in this case is between pencil and paper. Since this requires some advanced preparation, namely that you have your pencil in hand, a symbol might be useful as a signal to get prepared. This being our first attempt at making symbols, we will have to make it an especially good one.

In Italy during the Renaissance a word for "addition" was in common use. The Italian mathematicians found it awkward, however, to write the word out everytime they wanted to indicate addition. Instead, they decided to invent a symbol to use in place of the word. Their symbol became one of the first of many to signify a mathematical operation. They used the letter "p" as the basis for their new symbol, since "piu" (pronounced, unfortunately, as you might suspect) was the Italian word for "add," or more literally, "plus." The symbol itself was quite interest-ing— ℘ . With a little imagination and an original twist, this should serve our purpose quite well for it looks very much like a combination of the first letters of

$$\mathsf{G}_{et} \qquad \mathsf{Y}_{our} \qquad \mathsf{P}_{encil}$$

Putting these letters back together in composite form, we have a modern day "piu mark"

$$\wp$$

which henceforth will be the signal to "get your pencil."

2.3 VARIABLES

In most languages there are thousands of nouns that do not name any specific thing. One can use the word "boy," for instance, without having reference to a particular boy. Such nouns are called *common nouns*. In mathematics, symbols which have the same property as the common noun are called *variables*. A variable can represent a whole set of possible constants, but it cannot become a constant until it is positively identified as a specific constant or constants. In-troducing the notion of a variable to the mathematical language marks the graduation from arithmetic to algebra.

Constants and variables are not always as easily recognized in mathematics as in English. In English the use of the "article" helps in this identification. The definite article, "the," for instance, denotes reference to a particular noun—hence a constant. The indefinite articles, "a" and "an," denote nouns without positive identification —hence variables.

In most instances in mathematical usage one can determine whether a given symbol is a constant or a variable by recalling *the distinction between the symbol and its value.* For example, in the expression "$2m$" (which stands for the number m multiplied by the number 2) the "m" is treated as a variable, because any constant may be substituted for it, yielding perhaps $2(5)$ or $2(\frac{1}{2})$ or any other, as desired. In the statement "$2m = 4$" the "m" is *still* consid-ered to be a variable, even though some people might feel that since only $m = 2$ makes the statement true, that "m" is really a constant. Not so, of course, because any number that one chooses *can* be put in place of "m"—it's just that almost all such choices lead to false statements instead of the true one. To claim otherwise would be similar to claiming that a parking space in a lot ceases to be a parking space when assigned exclusively to one person. Variables can be likened to space holders, or blank spots, in which any of a collection of constants may be placed; some of these choices may be "against the law" in that they lead to an unacceptable state of affairs.

Before distinguishing between mathematical phrases (formulas) and mathematical sentences (equations), let us try out our new symbol.

1. Put a check mark in front of each of the following statements in which the symbol "X" is used as a variable:

_____"$X + X = 2X$"

_____" 'X' was preceded in the Presidency by Harry S. Truman"

_____"X is the 24th letter of the alphabet"

2.4 FORMULAS

The Cash Receipt is a familiar business form which, like most other blank forms, may be used to record a variety of transactions by filling in the blanks with various symbols. The Cash Receipt is a very simple form. It records time and place and other identifying information, then states in effect "X (the payer) has given Y (dollars) to Z (the payee)." To complete the form, one fills in the blanks with symbols, both numerals and words. The blank spaces on the receipt are acting as variables for which constants are substituted.

It is an easy step from form to formula. A *formula* is simply an expression containing one or more variables, which itself becomes a constant when constants are substituted for its variables. For instance, the formula "$A^2 + 2A$" becomes the constant "35" when the constant "5" is substituted for the variable "A." This substitution of constants into formulas is a very common operation in all mathematics, so some practice is in order.

2. Find the value of the following formulas when $x = a$ and $y = 2$. Write your answer in the space provided.

$x + a - ay$ _____

$2axy - a$ _____

3. Rewrite the following formulas using letters as symbols instead of words:

5% of sales plus 20% of gross margin _____

Fee minus Unfunded Overruns minus Income Previously Booked, all multiplied by the Portion of the Contract Complete.

Constants, variables, and formulas are referred to in mathematics as *terms*. There are many other symbols which are not terms, but are useful for making statements about terms. In the English language, the comma, parentheses, the colon, and the other punctuation marks are the most obvious of this kind. English words such as "and" and "or" are used to connect words to each other. Similarly, mathematical symbols such as " $+$ " and " $\div$ " are used to *connect* terms to each other, to form other terms. English words like "is," "becomes," and "has" have no meaning by themselves, but are essential to expressing thoughts with that language. In the language of mathematics, symbols such as $-$, $<$, and $\sqrt{}$ play a similar role.

These similarities between English and mathematics are reflected in the alternate readings of the statement "$2 + 2 = 4$" as "two *plus* two *equal* four" or "two *and* two *are* four." Just as one forms sentences with words, so does the mathematician form sentences using a vocabulary of terms and other symbols—sentences which look strange to those who have never learned that language, yet which, as we shall see, have an economy of space and a purity of meaning which justify their use.

In the following nonmathematical situation we can illustrate the first step in translating English into Algebra by using the symbols X and Y to help us in clarifying the matter of identity.

The situation using ordinary English is this:

A boy agreed with his chum to swap his roller skates for a bicycle for his sister. But the bicycle really belonged to the chum's sister who, when she heard about the arrangement, complained to her parents. The deal fell through and the boy who hoped to get the roller skates in return for his sister's bicycle and the boy whose sister was to have received the bicycle . . . that is, the boy who was going to exchange the roller skates for his sister . . . rather, the bicycle that was to have . . . .

We had better call in our lawyer:

The party of the first part offered his roller skates to the party of the second part in return for a bicycle. The sister of the party of the first part, hereinafter referred to as the second party of the first part, was to have received the bicycle, which in fact was the property of the sister of the party of the second part, hereinafter referred to as . . . .

Let us try X's and Y's instead:

X made a deal with Y to give Y X's roller skates in return for a bicycle for Miss X. Miss Y, the owner of the bicycle, objected. So Miss X didn't get the bicycle and Y didn't get the roller skates.

3. Elements of the Language

3.1 NUMBERS

The numbers we use in counting are called *natural numbers*, probably because one of the simplest characteristics to observe about objects that appear in nature is the characteristic of "how-manyness." The symbols we use to represent the natural numbers are the *numerals* 1, 2, 3, 4, 5. . . . This list can be extended indefinitely toward the right. All the numbers in the list of natural numbers are also called *whole numbers* or *positive integers*.

The development of mathematics has depended so heavily on the symbols we now use in writing the natural numbers, i.e., the system of numerals, that we sometimes fail to recognize it as one of the great inventions of the human mind. The system (the Hindu-Arabic numerals) developed over a period of more than a thousand years. One achievement of this system was the attachment of significance to the *position* of the numerals used in expressing a number. While this made it possible to express numbers as large as we please without inventing new symbols, it was just a by-product of a far more significant contribution; that was the invention of a symbol for "nothing" (the "howmanyness" represented by "none"), namely 0. The importance of this new symbol is inestimable, but we can get some idea by considering the problem of multiplying or dividing in a system without a zero such as the Roman numerals. The Romans, in fact, could not use their numeral system to multiply and divide; even addition and subtraction were not particularly convenient.

The historical process leading to the invention of zero and the speed with which the first grader acquires this concept, provide a striking contrast. The development process spanned centuries, but within hours the child is satisfied that it's a very good idea to have a name for the number representing "none" or "nothing." Having learned to write the names of the natural numbers and zero (which is not considered to be one of the natural numbers), the child today is ready to draw pictures and play games that are new to his generation. A picture called a "number line" is used to represent zero and the set of all the natural numbers. This device is simply a geometric representation formed by assigning zero to a point on a straight line and assigning the natural numbers, in order, to equidistant points on the line to the right of zero.

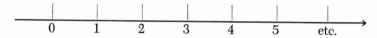

The first appearance of *negative* numbers dates back to the Hindus of the twelfth century. It took nearly 500 years for this idea to become an accepted part of the study of algebra. Surprising as it may seem several centuries passed before anyone even attempted to attach a concrete meaning to the mysterious negative numbers. One of the early recorded interpretations was made by a medieval Italian mathematician named Fibonacci. Fibonacci suggested that a business loss could be viewed as negative profit; and with this seemingly simple discovery, negative numbers started the long descent from the blue sky of pure mathematical abstraction into service in practical problems. If you were attending grammar school today, you would not find it at all unreasonable to learn that your number line was really incomplete. It can just as well be extended indefinitely to the left of zero to include the symbols − 1, − 2, − 3. . . . These new numbers (again excluding zero) are called *negative integers*.

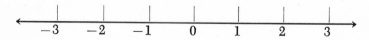

This new number line which now includes the *negative integers, zero,* and the *natural numbers* contains the set of *all* integers; and, by definition, any integer on this line is *larger* than all integers lying to its left and *smaller* than all integers lying to its right.

In the exercise below, insert the word "larger" or "smaller" in the blank spaces provided.

4. + 2 is _____ than + 8
   − 3 is _____ than 0
   − 5 is _____ than − 3
   + 6 is _____ than 0
     0 is _____ than − 2

5. Two perpendicular lines, each containing the set of all integers, are called *co-ordinate axes*. The point of intersection of the lines is the zero point on each scale and is called the *origin*. Mark the scale of integers on each of the perpendicular lines.

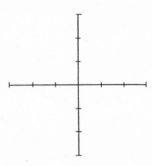

In the new mathematics curricula used in many grammar schools, the painful task of raising the issue of fractions falls on the fourth grade teacher. With the aid of the number line and other devices, this is probably a lot less painful than our recollections of this transition. The children are usually pleased to learn that those spaces they had been saving between the integers on the number line are an excellent place to put new points representing fractions. In this manner the children are able to visualize where fractions fit in the number scheme. They learn that, if x and y are integers, x/y is a *fraction*. They discover that some fractions are already represented by points on the line of integers, for instance $\frac{6}{3} = 2, \frac{-8}{4} = -2$, etc., while others like $\frac{3}{8}$ are points lying between two integers. In other words, fractions can do what integers do and then some; and the number line is no longer the set of all integers, but the set of all *rational numbers* (i.e., numbers that can be formed by the *ratio* of two integers). They also learn a more precise meaning of "equal." Two rational numbers are equal only if they can be represented by the same point on the number line. For example,

$\dfrac{6}{24} = \dfrac{1}{4}$ but $\dfrac{90}{125} \neq \dfrac{91}{125}$ ($\neq$ is read "does not equal") because these two fractions correspond to different points.

6. Circle the answers that apply.

$\dfrac{2}{7}$ is a $\begin{cases} \text{positive integer} \\ \text{rational number} \\ \text{fraction} \end{cases}$

-3 is a $\begin{cases} \text{rational number} \\ \text{negative integer} \\ \text{natural number} \end{cases}$

0 is a $\begin{cases} \text{fraction} \\ \text{integer} \\ \text{natural number} \end{cases}$

7. Find a rational number between $\dfrac{5}{13}$ and $\dfrac{7}{18}$. ——————————

Let us now summarize the types of numbers we have defined.

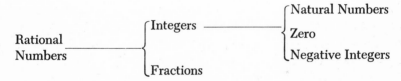

The rational numbers include all integers and all fractions formed by dividing one integer by another. All integers include all natural numbers, all negative integers, and zero.

3.2 OPERATIONS WITH NUMBERS

Notice that when we extended the line representing the natural numbers to the left through zero to include the negative integers, we left the realm of arithmetic, where we were restricted to positive numbers, i.e., where 2 minus 4 was undefined, and entered the realm of algebra. In the process our concept of number assumes new power and meaning, for one number can now have two qualities: *magnitude* and *direction*. The direction is supplied to a number by its sign. A change in temperature of 10°, for example, indicates a change in magnitude only. A change in temperature of $+10°$ or $-10°$, on the other hand, indicates the direction of the change as well, plus (+) for a rise in temperature and minus (−) for a drop in temperature. Likewise, while it is important to know that profits have changed by a certain number of dollars from one period to another, it is equally important to know the direction of the change. Numbers having both magnitude and direction are sometimes called *algebraic* or *directed* numbers.

The natural numbers may be represented by numerals with or without the prefix of a plus sign (+). In either case, a positive integer is understood, e.g., 10 = + 10. The negative integers, on the other hand, must be prefixed by the minus sign (−). But this convention of interpreting the unsigned numeral as positive creates a problem. How then can we indicate those occasions when we wish to specify the magnitude only, and not the direction, of a number? In our numeral system, this problem is not completely solved; that is, if a numeral representing a natural number is prefixed by a plus sign it is clear that direction as well as magnitude is intended. However, if it is left unsigned, it is not clear which is intended. In algebraic work, this lack of clarity cannot be tolerated. To solve this problem a special name and symbol were invented. The name is *absolute value* and the symbol is two vertical lines, one on either side of the variable whose magnitude only is intended. For example, if P represents the change in profit dollars then P could conceivably be a positive or negative number. If for some reason we were concerned with only the magnitude of the change, we could indicate this by $|P|$, read as "the absolute value of P."

In the exercises below, fill in the blanks from the words provided.

8. $|-3|$ is _____ than $|-2|$
   larger/smaller

9. $|+5|$ is _____ than $|-8|$
   larger/smaller

10. The absolute value of -3 is _____ than the absolute value of -2.
    larger/smaller

11. $|-3|$ is _____ than $|0|$
    larger/smaller

12. Given that A and B are positive integers, and that A is larger than B, encircle each of the following expressions that can be represented by a positive integer:

   $|-A|$
   $-A - |-B|$
   $|A| + |B|$

Until fairly recently the tricky business of teaching children to add and subtract directed numbers was not entrusted to the grammar school teacher. This took a specialist, the junior high algebra teacher. In the new math curricula such matters are covered early in grammar school. The number line now serves as the playing field for a new kind of game, and the chief players are imaginary crickets that crawl and jump back and forth along the line. (The cricket can usually tell what grade he's in by the kind of numbers he's landing on.)

To illustrate, to add + 3 to a + 2, the cricket must leave the comfort of his home at zero and take two jumps to the right, one of 3 units and one of 2 units.

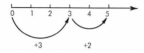

He ends up 5 units away from home and sitting on the answer to an algebra problem. Negative numbers cause him to jump to the left and a subtraction sign causes him to turn around and do just the opposite of what he would normally do. For instance, (+ 3) − (− 2) would require him to jump three units to the right, get ready to jump two units to the left but then turn around and jump the two units to the right. He ends up sitting on + 5 again. The cricket, of course, soon becomes more trouble than he's worth and is discarded but not before his playmates *know* such things as "to add numbers of the same sign, add their absolute values and prefix the common sign"—and without ever learning this as one of a list of algebraic rules. Most of us learned the rules the hard way and when we were four or five years older.

The four basic rules for adding and subtracting directed numbers are illustrated below:

1. *Adding numbers of the same sign:*
   $(+ 2) + (+ 3) + (+ 1) = 6$
   $(- 2) + (- 3) + (- 1) = - 6$
   (Add the absolute values and prefix the common sign.)

2. *Adding numbers of different signs:*
   $(+ 2) + (- 3) = - 1$
   (Find the difference between the absolute values first, then prefix the sign of the larger.)

3. *Adding several numbers:*
   $(+ 2) + (- 3) + (+ 1) + (- 2) = - 2$

(Add the positive and negative numbers separately, then use rule 2 above.)

4. *To subtract one from another:*
$$(+1) - (-3) = 4$$
$$(+1) - (+3) = -2$$
(Change the sign of the number to be subtracted, then proceed as if it were algebraic addition.)

These rules apply to problems involving the symbols for numbers that are known, i.e., numerals. But what about the symbols for numbers that are not known—like variables? In this case, some of the arithmetic operations cannot be completed until later, when the actual numbers for which the variables stand are specified. For example, the formula $(x + 2)$ cannot be further simplified until the number represented by the symbol "x" is given. If x is found to equal $+3$, then $x + 2$ would equal 5. If $x = -2$, then the addition would yield zero. Similarly, if the formula $(2x + 3y)$ were written, in which the variables x and y are to be multiplied by 2 and 3 respectively, and the results added, these actual operations must await knowledge of the numerical values of x and y. Of course, the formula $3x + 2x - x + b$ can be simplified to $4x + b$, since the result is true no matter what value is finally assigned to the variable x.

13. Perform the indicated additions and subtractions:

$$(-1) + (+4) + (-5) = \underline{\qquad}$$
$$-1 + \quad 4 - 5 \quad = \underline{\qquad}$$
$$(-3x - 2y + 5) + (-x - 5y) = \underline{\qquad}$$
$$-3x - 2y + 5 \ - x - 5y \quad = \underline{\qquad}$$

The rules for *multiplying* and *dividing* directed numbers can be stated as follows:

1. When two numbers have *like* signs their product is *positive* and their quotient is *positive*.
$$2(3) = 6 \qquad\qquad (-2)(-3) = 6$$
$$\frac{4}{2} = 2 \qquad\qquad \frac{-4}{-2} = 2$$

2. When two numbers have *unlike* signs their product is *negative* and their quotient is *negative*.
$$-2(3) = -6 \qquad\qquad (-2)(+3) = -6$$
$$\frac{-4}{2} = -2 \qquad\qquad \frac{4}{-2} = -2$$

3. When a product contains an even number of negative factors it is *positive;* when it contains an odd number of negative factors it is *negative.*

$$(-2)(-3) = 6 \qquad\qquad 2(-3) = -6$$
$$(-2)(-3)(-4) = -24 \qquad (-2)(-3)(+4) = 24$$

Apply these rules to the following exercises. (Note: do not feel bad if you have difficulty with number 15. This is a big jump from the material covered in the paragraph above.)

14. Perform the indicated operations:

$$(5)(2) = \underline{\hspace{3cm}}$$

$$(5)(2)(-2) = \underline{\hspace{3cm}}$$

$$\frac{(5)(2)(-2)}{(-2)} = \underline{\hspace{3cm}}$$

$$\frac{(+5)(+2)(-2)}{(4-2)} = \underline{\hspace{3cm}}$$

15. If two integers are each selected at random (from the list of all positive and negative integers), what is the chance that their product will be an odd negative integer?

Answer: \underline{\hspace{4cm}}.

3.3 SOME VOCABULARY

Our analogy of mathematics to a language would be incomplete without including a basic vocabulary of conventional mathematical symbols. A partial list, to which we will add as required, is provided below. A few of the symbols have been used already; others will be further clarified as we have occasion to use them.

Symbol	English Translation
$=$	equals, is equal to
$\neq$	is not equal to
$\equiv$	identical, is identical to
$\not\equiv$	is not identical to
$<$	is less than
$\leq$	is less than or equal to
$>$	greater than
$\geq$	greater than or equal to
$\lvert a \rvert$	absolute value of "a"

Symbol	English Translation
$+$	add (or plus, or positive)
$-$	subtract (or minus, or negative)
$\pm$	plus or minus
ab	the product, "a" times "b"
$\dfrac{a}{b}$	the quotient, "a" divided by "b"
$\sqrt{a}$	the square root of "a," i.e., the number which when multiplied by itself will equal "a."
a^2	the square of "a," i.e., "a" multiplied by itself
a^n	"a" raised to the nth power, i.e., "a" multiplied by itself n times
a_1, a_2, a_3	("1," "2," and "3" are called *subscripts* and act like adjectives to identify *which* "a.")
$\displaystyle\sum_{i=1}^{n} a_i$	the sum of all the individual subscripted a's, starting with a_1 and ending with a_n; that is, $(a_1 + a_2 + a_3 + \ldots a_n)$.
$\Sigma\, a$	an abbreviated form for "the sum of all "a's," used in cases where there is no possibility of confusing which "a's" are to be summed
	get your pencil.

As we mentioned earlier, the mathematician is free to invent symbolic names as he sees fit for the constants and variables he will deal with in a particular problem. (To illustrate this, we invented one of our own.) This matter of assigning symbolic names is called *notation.*

While notation is a matter of personal preference, it is influenced by the use to be made of the symbols. For instance, the use of the subscript notation illustrated above is a commonly used and very convenient way to distinguish among large groups of similar variables. If a computer is to be used, the notation must be compatible with the computer language. The objective in notation selection is to make it concise, explicit, and understandable to others with a minimum of explanation.

3.4 IN SUMMARY

In this unit we have discussed mathematics in terms of its development and its characteristic feature of using special names and symbols. In closing, let us consider some of the problems with viewing mathematics in these terms.

First, let us consider the matter of special symbolism. We were led to compare mathematics with English and concluded that mathematics has many of the characteristics of a language. It is possible, in fact, to communicate mathematically using almost no English at all. However, every mathematical statement can also be restated in English without the use of special mathematical symbolism. The results would usually be awkward and inconvenient, but the very possibility shows that the symbolic notation of mathematics is not mathematics itself. Indeed, to say otherwise is to confuse the symbols with their use. Remember, mathematics is the subject expressed by these symbols; mathematics is not the symbols themselves.

We discussed the development of mathematics in terms of its being a science of number and a science of space. But this, too, creates problems. The child, for instance, first meets mathematics when he learns to count and do simple problems involving numbers. As he learns more and more arithmetic he thinks of mathematics as having to do with more and more complicated calculations with numbers. As he advances to high school, he finds that geometry is also a part of mathematics. At this point he is satisfied with defining mathematics as a science of number and space; this is a generally accepted view. And it is not surprising, for this is how mathematics developed and how it was taught for centuries. The problem with this view is that mathematics is too broad to be characterized as dealing solely with the concepts of number and space.

In the units which follow, we will be attempting to gain a better understanding of some of the things that mathematicians do that have relevance to business management. In the process other fundamental concepts, in addition to number and space, will come into our view of mathematics.

CHAPTER 2

Organizing Statistical Data

1. Introduction

1.1 WHAT IS/ARE STATISTICS?

In this chapter and in Chapters 3 and 5 our attention will focus on the *science of statistics*. The word "science" indicates that we have reference to a particular body of knowledge—in this case, the body of knowledge concerned with methods of dealing with numerical data. The "numerical data" is obtained from observation or measurement; and the "methods" relate to collecting, classifying, analyzing, interpreting, and drawing conclusions from the data. More concisely, statistics is *the science of drawing conclusions from observations.*

The word "statistics" may also be used with reference, not to the body of statistical knowledge, but to the numerical data itself or measures derived from numerical data. In this sense "statistics" is plural, rather than singular. "Payroll statistics" is such a plural use of the word. A single number used in this same sense is a statistic. Net sales billed, for example, is a statistic. And in the title of this chapter the words "statistical data" are synonymous with numerical data.

While this double meaning may appear confusing, the context in which "statistics" is used will usually make clear which meaning is intended.

 1. The noted British statesman Disraeli is reputed to have claimed that, "There are three kinds of lies: lies, damned lies, and statistics."

Below are some statements regarding this claim. Indicate your opinion as to whether each statement is true or false by marking a T or F in the space provided:

Statistics as used by Disraeli is singular. _____

Disraeli has reference to the science of statistics. _____

Disraeli is suspicious of numerical "facts." _____

Disraeli, we suspect, had reference to a fact that you are already well aware of, and that is, that statistics (numerical data) can be quite misleading. You are also aware of statistics (again, numerical data) that on the contrary to being misleading, are most helpful in understanding complex situations. A familiar example is the balance sheet. The balance sheet is an orderly and understandable summary of the financial state of a business—a state at which the business has arrived as a result of an extremely large number of individual transactions. Although few people think of the balance sheet as an example of the science of statistics, the basic principles of statistical description and the fact that the balance sheet does contain such a wealth of information are neither unrelated nor accidental.

There is an important difference between statistics of the kind that fit Disraeli's claim and the statistics contained on the balance sheet, and the difference is the adherence to basic statistical principles. This difference has influenced administrators of academic programs in the fields of business and economics to include courses in statistics in their curricula. This same difference led H. G. Wells, the noted historian, to predict in the early 1920's that a knowledge of statistics "will one day be as necessary to efficient citizenship as the ability to read or write." This was a bold prediction; but, at least as it applies to business problems and the measurement or control function of management, it is coming true in our time. The payoff will most certainly be more informed decision making.

1.2 STATISTICS AND PROBABILITIES

Statistics and probability are so often referred to in the same breath that the nature of the differences between the two terms may be confused. The confusion stems from the fact that both probability theory and statistics approach the same target, but they do so from opposite directions. In a probability problem, the contributing factors are known. For instance, if you were given a pair of dice and were asked to examine them, you would observe that each die has six sides. This observation might lead you to conclude that there would be an equal likelihood of any one side appearing if one die were rolled. This leads directly to conclusions regarding the probability of rolling a deuce, for instance. What you do not know for certain is whether a deuce will appear if you were to pick up a die and roll it right now.

In statistics the problem is just reversed. You know what the results are because you can observe them, but you do not know all you would like to know about the process that is causing the results you observe. If you had never seen a die and had only a tabulation of the results of many rolls of a die, you would conclude that the process causing the results apparently produces numbers from one through six with equal likelihood. This is pretty much the same information as before but arrived at from a different direction. In the probability case, you were concerned with knowing something of the results to expect. In the statistical case, the matter of concern is the process producing the results observed. Stated more simply, statistics uses results that are already known to understand a process that is not fully revealed. Probability theory uses a knowledge of the process to determine the likelihood of a particular unrevealed future result.

1.3 STATISTICAL DESCRIPTION VERSUS STATISTICAL INFERENCE

Statistics may be as esoteric and as highly mathematical as one cares to make it. Consideration of the subject here, however, will be limited to the more important of the basic principles—principles which fortunately are both the least complicated and the most useful.

In this text we shall be limiting our coverage of statistics to matters of *statistical description*. In a separate text we shall cover *statistical inference*. Since many authors do not explicitly distinguish matters involving inference from those that are essentially descriptive, we had better note the distinction at this point.

Statistical description relates to methods of describing numerical data. It is the link between the act of collecting numerical data and the problem of comprehending the data once it has been collected. *Statistical inference* is another—although closely related—matter. This concerns the task of drawing conclusions which transcend the data at hand and apply to a larger body of data that has not been completely collected. (The "larger body of data" and the "process," mentioned in the previous paragraph, that appeared to produce the numerals from one through six with equal likelihood, are equivalent.)

As one might imagine, the task of drawing valid conclusions or inferences is dependent on first comprehending the data that is already available. Comprehension, unfortunately, does not follow automatically from data collection. To be meaningful the data, once collected, must be adequately described. Data is described by organizing it and presenting it so that its information content is most readily communicated. Essentially this involves:

Arranging masses of data so they are more understandable.

Presenting the data in ways that focus attention on significant characteristics.

Summarizing the data by means of a few important measures.

The conversion of masses of data to useful information is an area in which the statistician makes some of his most useful contributions. This work must precede and, in fact, makes possible the drawing of valid inferences.

It must be recognized, however, that almost any group of observations or data is a *sample* from a larger group representing things as they really are or will be. Things as they really are—or the real world from which the sample is drawn—are ordinarily referred to in statistics as the *universe* or *population*. What is exactly true for the sample is typically only approximately true for the universe. The degree of approximation may be excellent or it may be worthless. In fact, measuring this degree of approximation is one common problem of statistical inference. The following example—in this case, of poor statistical inference—illustrates the importance of the difference between a *sample* and the *universe*:

In 1936 FDR was opposed in the presidential election by Alf Landon. In the interest of keeping its readers informed, the *Literary Digest* conducted a poll for the purpose of prognosticating the result—a prognostication that was to become famous. A gigantic sample of ten million telephone and *Digest* subscribers assured the editors that Landon would win by a margin of better than 2 to 1. The *Digest* announced the landslide—later to discover, of course, that while their sample elected Landon, the voters elected Roosevelt. The Sunday morning quarterbacks were quick to recognize that those who could afford telephones and magazine subscriptions in 1936 were not a cross-section of the voters. Poor application of statistical inference resulted in a sample loaded with what turned out to be Republican voters.

The distinction between description and inference, although simple to comprehend, is often lost sight of in practice as the *Literary Digest* experience illustrates. Too often the evidence brought to light by the statistical description of a *sample* is so engrossing that the need to draw inferences about the *universe* is forgotten, or much worse, inferences are drawn without regard for the possibility of a discrepancy existing between the state of the sample and the true state of the universe.

 2. See if you can recognize the difference between a statistical description and a statistical inference in the following statements.

Circle One

Four out of the ten American League ball clubs have changed managers in the last two years.	Stat. Desc.	Stat. Inf.
Three out of ten wage earners in the United States are salaried.	Stat. Desc.	Stat. Inf.
In a discussion regarding expense accounts, the internal auditor stated that a recent sampling of expense accounts showed the average charge for breakfast to be $0.75.	Stat. Desc.	Stat. Inf.

You have just read an ad that made the claim that "nine out of ten New York doctors prefer (Brand X)."

Is it possible that this is a statistical description?	Yes	No
Is it possible that this is a statistical inference?	Yes	No

2. Numerical Data

2.1 NUMBERS AND THE REAL WORLD

The substantive work of statistical description begins with numerical data. But numerical data is, itself, symbolic. The significance of the data lies, not in the groups of numerals, but in the real world events and circumstances that gave rise to the data. For data to be useful, its source must be clearly understood and well defined; and no amount of arithmetic, however accurate, can substitute for this understanding.

Consider a number labeled "number of passenger automobiles produced in the United States during the week ended August 26, 1956." Did someone stand at the end of the assembly lines tallying finished units? If so, was every line included, and was the tallying perfectly accurate? And how were all the separate counts compiled for the total figure? Perhaps each manufacturer reported his own figures, some based on production schedules, some on the number of engines sent to the assembly line, and some on the number of automobiles not only off the assembly line but also approved on a final inspection process. What of cars partially produced during the week; do two half-finished cars count as one, and if so, when is a car half-finished? What of production of parts for shipment abroad unassembled?"[1]

Suppose the "number of automobiles produced" had in fact been determined by an accurate tally of each unit as it rolled off the production line. Would not this number be a good measure of the productive activity of the automobile industry? But what if a new production line was just opening? There would surely be a large amount of productive activity on incomplete units that would not be reflected in this tally; or if a line were about to be closed, there would be tallies recorded for cars on which only a few final steps were taken during the relevant period. In other words, "numbers of automobiles produced" determined by end-of-line tallies may be an excellent measure if this were precisely the quantity of interest. It would be a poor measure, however, of the total productive activity of the industry.

The following example further illustrates the importance of understanding the relationship that numbers bear to the subject matter under consideration:

A certain museum in a major New England city took great pride in its amazing attendance record. Plans were underway to expand on the basis of the interest shown by the public through their attendance. Before the expansion plans materialized, however, the city erected a little stone building nearby. The next year the attendance mysteriously fell

---

[1] W. Allen Wallis and Harry V. Roberts, *Statistics: A New Approach* (Glencoe, Ill.: Free Press, 1956), p. 132.

off by more than 100,000. What was the little stone building? A comfort station.[2]

2.2 QUALITY OF DATA

Cold, hard numbers have the unusual characteristic of creating an illusion of rightness. Under this influence people are easily lured into uncritical thinking. You have no doubt witnessed a verbal version of this if you have ever participated in a conversation that has been stopped cold by someone's quotation of "the figures." That "the figures" frequently have no basis in fact is usually immaterial.

This is pure nonsense, of course. Numbers are not sacred and, in fact, are subject to ambiguities that can prevent them from containing the information you may think they contain. The presence or absence of these ambiguities is a measure of data *quality*.

One measure of data quality is *validity*. A number or numbers are said to be *valid* if they *measure what they purport to measure*. The number of people entering the front door of the museum mentioned earlier was certainly not a valid measure of the number of people attending the museum for cultural reasons. Neither was the end-of-line tally of automobiles a valid measure of productive activity in the automobile industry.

Another measure of data quality is *accuracy*. *Accuracy* is a measure of *the difference between the data and the actual or true value* of whatever the data represents. For instance, a man's weight may have been measured to the nearest pound as 170. A more accurate measure of the same man's weight might be 169.87 pounds at the moment of weighing. In general, barring mistakes or systematic errors, the accuracy of data can be improved by refining the instruments or improving the methods by which the data is gathered.

Still another measure of data quality is *precision*. This is a measure of the *repeatability* of the data. That is, if the same measurement or observation were taken on the same object on two separate occasions, would the same data result? If it were the same or very close, the measurements and the resulting data would be precise. It is entirely possible, of course, for data to be precise without being accurate. If measurements were obtained by very carefully weighing something on a scale that consistently indicates five pounds

---

[2] Adapted from *This Week*, April 17, 1948. (Quoted in *ibid.*, p. 133.)

heavy, for instance, the results might be precise, but inaccurate. In general, precision is improved by taking more care in the data collection or measurement process.[3]

Based on the above statistical definitions circle the relevant measure of data quality under each exercise below:

3. A certain inspector has been instructed to keep a tally of the color of refrigerator door panels passing his inspection station. After collecting the data it is learned that the inspector is color blind and always recognized pink as green. The resulting data would lack:

Validity   Accuracy   Precision

4. On two separate occasions the same person took an I.Q. test and achieved very nearly the same score both times. This is an indication of the test's:

Validity   Accuracy   Precision

5. Overhead expense has been allocated to product lines in proportion to the numbers on the automobile license plates of the product line managers. Such an allocation would certainly lack:

Validity   Accuracy   Precision

6. Could the license plate ratios be accurate?

Yes   No

Be precise?

Yes   No

Evaluation of data quality in a practical situation can, of course, be much more deceptive than these exercises indicate. There are a number of technical procedures and tests that can be used. There are also a number of simple common-sense checks that can provide clues as to the quality of data. Independent of the approach used, evaluation hinges on:

A knowledge of what information the data is to provide, and
How the data was obtained.

To elaborate: What do you want to learn from the data? What decisions will be made? What conclusions will be drawn? In short, is the data appropriate for the use intended? Is a yardstick being

---

[3] Frequently used synonyms for precision and validity are *reliability* and *relevance*, respectively.

used when micrometers are required? Are micrometers being used when a yardstick would suffice? (This is expensive.)

Occasionally the data, itself, will contain internal clues as to its quality. Absurd or impossible values are obviously in error. A weekly salary of $150,000, for instance, has too many decimal places. (It may have other problems as well.) Annual sales of $13.27 is a figure at least deficient of decimal places. Certain kinds of regularity or irregularity are also suspicious. Two successive monthly income figures of $101,250 would certainly appear questionable. So might the next to last number in the following series of overhead loading factors: 1.33, 1.36, 1.35, 2.37, 1.39.

It is important to note here that while the business manager might not be skilled in the science of statistics, he *is* skilled in judgments regarding data quality. His contribution to a statistical study therefore is of considerable importance at this point.

7. The following are the death rates in 1951 of infants under one week of age:

Age (days) . . .	0–1	1–2	2–3	3–4	4–5	5–6	6–7
Deaths per 1,000 .	9.8	3.1	(blur)	1.1	0.6	0.5	0.3

Of the numbers below circle the one you would most expect to find in place of the blur: 0.2 1.2 2.1 5.9

8. 4 (blur) 16 25 36

Circle the number below that you would expect to find in place of the blur: 5 9 12 ?

(Would it influence your answer any if you had the following additional information? The numbers listed are the numbers on the jerseys of the five heaviest men on the high school football team.)

3.   Observations

3.1 WHAT IS AN OBSERVATION?

Basic facts in a statistical investigation are in the form of numerical data. Each individual fact in the data is called an *observation* because it has been observed in some manner (either measured or counted) and then recorded.

A distinction is drawn between the *items observed* and an *observation*. The *items observed* collectively comprise the *sample* referred to earlier. The sample, you may recall, was drawn from a *universe*, and the universe was the aggregate of all the individual items of interest, called *elementary units,* in a particular problem situation. The *items observed* have certain measurable or observable characteristics or traits that are relevant to the problem at hand. These traits or characteristics are called *variables.* Each *observation* then is a measure of the variables for one elementary unit included in the sample.

To help clarify these terms, suppose you wished to determine the average life of the standard 100-watt lamp currently being produced in your plant. In this problem the *universe* would include all the 100-watt lamps made to date or yet to be produced as long as the design, materials, and manufacturing process remain unchanged. Individual lamps are the *elementary units* in this universe, and those lamps selected for testing comprise the *sample.* The lamps in the sample will be the *items observed.* Lamp life is the *variable* of interest, and a test would be conducted so this variable could be measured. Each *observation* then would be a number representing the measured time before a particular test lamp burned out.

9. You wish to determine the average income of the wage earners in your community.

What is the universe in this case? _____

What is the variable? _____

(Might you anticipate any problems of data quality in making such a determination?)

10. You have been assigned the task of assisting the judges in a beauty contest in which there are 50 contestants. Your task essentially involves taking the necessary measurements required to provide the judges with three numerical facts per girl. (Any additional facts you may gather need not be recorded.)

What are the items observed? _____

Think about (but do not write down) the variables to be measured.

How many measurements would be involved? _____

3.2 PROPERTIES OF A UNIVERSE

You may have noted a difference in the nature of the universe in the illustration using 100-watt lamps and the universe in either of the exercises above. Included in the universe of lamps were not only those that are presently in existence, but all those that might be produced in the future by the same process under the same operating conditions. Conceivably the process could continue without change indefinitely. In such a case the universe is regarded as *infinite*.

The exercises, on the other hand, involved situations in which the universe had a definite size. In these cases the universe was *finite*. Roughly speaking, a universe is finite if it is comprised of a definite number of elementary units. The size of the number or ability to physically count the units has no bearing on the classification. A universe comprised of the entire male population of the United States, for instance, would be finite, although certainly impossible to physically count.

3.3 PROPERTIES OF A VARIABLE

The variable in the lamp illustration, you may recall, was lamp life; it was measured in terms of numbers of hours. Variables like lamp life that require a measure having magnitude are called *quantitative* variables.

Quantitative variables are classed as either *continuous* or *discrete*. *Continuous* means that the variable can assume any numerical value within a particular range. For instance, a dimensional measure can be divided into fractional parts of any size, limited in practice only by the equipment used to measure the dimension. In theory any two such dimensions will always be separated by some fraction, however small. Weight, length, and time are common examples of continuous variables. In business problems other examples occur in variables such as indices (e.g., a price index or a productivity index), also in rates and ratios such as overhead or profit rates. Continuous variables of this latter kind are not the result of direct observation. Most frequently they result from arithmetic operations like the dividing of one number by another. An overhead expense of $10 and a direct expense of $3 produce the rate of 333.33 · · %, for example.

Discrete variables, in contrast, change in definite increments and cannot assume a numerical value between the increments. Money, for example, is discrete in the sense that you can pay a man only to the nearest cent. People are discrete in the sense that they can only be counted as integers, i.e., whole numbers. An observation of a fractional part of either pennies or people is meaningless.

This applies only to observations, however. In some cases it is not only useful but necessary to consider these variables as though they were continuous. Cases where more than two figures must be carried to the right of the decimal in a dollar figure, e.g., hourly wage rates, are examples.

This distinction, discrete as opposed to continuous variables, is largely theoretical and is useful in the selection of analytic processes. In practical work, however, the distinction is only approximate. Things as discrete as runs scored and innings pitched (discrete in thirds of innings) are combined in the calculation of a continuous "earned run average." If it is decided that this average is to be carried to only two decimal places, then this too becomes discrete. While the time to run the mile is theoretically measured on a continuous scale, measuring equipment limitations have necessitated that records be maintained in units that are discrete to tenths of seconds.

Not all variables, of course, require measures of magnitude. Suppose, for example, you were asked the per cent of employees in your component having more than ten years service. Assume that the service dates were readily available and that you were about to compile the data required to make the calculation. Notice that each observation would provide information regarding whether a particular employee had ten years service or not; one or the other. The fact that an individual had 11 or 25 years would be immaterial. Variables of this kind are classed as *qualitative* variables, as opposed to quantitative variables requiring a measure of magnitude. The classifications of discrete and continuous *do not* apply to qualitative variables.

The following summary may help clarify the distinctions between the types of variables:

Qualitative . . if the variable involves *classifying* the item observed according to a characteristic or attribute.

Quantitative . . if the variable involves *measuring* the item observed; the measurements have magnitude and are usually expressed in numerical terms.

   Continuous . . .if the measurement is theoretically infinitely divisible.

   Discrete . . . .if the measurement cannot be divided below a certain limiting increment without losing its identity or meaning.

 11. How would you classify the variable in a problem involving determination of the seating capacity in a cafeteria?

Circle one in each row

| Discrete | Continuous | Neither |
| Quantitative | Qualitative | Neither |

12. In a determination of the number of components over or under budget the variable would be:

| Discrete | Continuous | Neither |
| Quantitative | Qualitative | Neither |

3.4 MORE THAN ONE VARIABLE

In most of the situations mentioned thus far only one variable was involved. (The beauty contest was an exception.) In the one variable situation, for each observation there was only one fact regarding the elementary unit that was of interest, hence 100 observations result in the recording of 100 facts. Such observations are called *univariate*.

There are many instances, however, when the matter of interest is the association between two or more variables. Suppose, for example, you were concerned with the relationship between salary and age of employees. In this case the elementary units are employees, but there are now two variables of interest. For each employee you would observe two facts: his age and his salary. Furthermore these facts must be *cross-classified*. That is, they must be recorded so that the age and salary of a single individual are always associated with each other. The fact that one man's age is 50 and another's annual salary is $7,000 would be of no help at all. In such cases the observations are called *bivariate*. In the beauty contest they were *trivariate*, and proper association was maintained by recording the data in the familiar top-to-bottom sequence, i.e., 36–24–36.

4. Organizing Data

4.1 ORGANIZATION IN TABULAR FORM

Having touched briefly on some of the ideas, terms, and considerations basic to all statistical work, we now turn to the work of statistical description.

Information regarding events of the past is frequently useful in drawing inferences about the future. But events of the past can never be measured or observed directly again. Information, therefore, must be obtained indirectly from data that is already in existence. In many business problems, relevant data can be found in abundance. In fact, notebooks, desk drawers, and file cabinets contain far more data than ever gets converted into useful information for decision making. This is often the starting point in statistical description, i.e., a mass of numerical data that is already available. And the first step is to organize or arrange the data in ways that make it understandable and useful.

To illustrate, consider the following example:

The Precision Connector line was originally begun to provide customers with a source of connectors that would match the precision of the products in the Test Equipment line. Since then, however, high quality connectors have become generally available through a number of specialty suppliers and the line is now considered marginal. The General Manager has requested that an extensive analysis be conducted and, as a Cost Analyst, you have been appointed to the investigating task force.

To get a better understanding of the way customers buy connectors, you have decided to check the quantities purchased per requisition for the last 6 months starting with the Type D Connector. The "Requisition File" in Customer Billing is a reliable source for this information. At this moment, however, the file is no more useful than:

A Pile of Data

The first step in sorting out this mess is accomplished by simply transferring the order quantities of Type D Connectors from the requisitions for the last six months to a single sheet of paper. Thirty orders were found in the following quantities:

100	58	70
78	65	86
98	42	91
103	64	109
80	90	75
75	89	51
48	60	75
65	85	97
83	68	80
53	74	77

Customer Order Quantities
Type D Connector (1/1–6/30)

This string of numbers is an improvement but it is still not very revealing. The greater the number of observations, of course, the more confusing such an array of data would be. It would help if the numbers were sorted out and rearranged in either ascending or descending numerical *order*. This new arrangement, shown below, is called an *ordered array:*

Ordered Array

42	70	85
48	74	86
51	75	89
53	75	90
58	75	91
60	77	97
64	78	98
65	80	100
65	80	103
68	83	109

Type D Connector Order Quantities

At a glance now we see that the order quantity varied from 42 to 109. Half the time the orders were for 75 units or less; half the time, for 77 or more. Most of the time the orders were for quantities of between 60 and 90 units. At this point the usefulness of the ordered array is pretty much exhausted.

A more useful device, particularly where large numbers of observations are involved, is the *frequency table* or *frequency distribution*. A frequency table is constructed by dividing the range over which the observations vary into a convenient number of smaller ranges called *class intervals*. The frequencies with which observations occur is then recorded within each of the intervals. The following is an example using the data already collected:

Frequency Table

	Order Quantity	Number of Observations	
	Less than 40	0	
	40–50	2	
	50–60	3	
	60–70	5	
Class Intervals	70–80	7	Frequencies
	80–90	6	
	90–100	4	
	110–110	3	
	110 or more	0	
		30	

Customer Order Quantities of Type D Connectors

In this table nine class intervals have been used. Except for the extremes at either end the range of each interval is ten units. This table is constructed directly from the ordered array. For example, the ordered array contains two observations (42 and 48 units) within the interval from 40 to 50 units. Within this interval, therefore, the number of observations, or frequency, is two.

Note that the end of one range is the same as the beginning of the next. For instance, 50 is used as the upper limit in the interval from 40 to 50 and the lower limit in the interval from 50 to 60. The general convention is that the range of the class interval begins with the lower value and includes all values *up to but not including* the upper value. The observation 70, therefore, belongs in the 70 to 80 interval, not the 60 to 70 interval.

The frequency table has most of the advantages of the ordered array and the further advantage of summarizing the data to point up the salient features of its distribution. It has the disadvantage of submerging some of the details and making some kinds of further analyses less convenient. Selection of the number of class intervals is an important consideration here, since different choices can lead to entirely different pictures. For this reason it is best to start with an ample number of intervals. The number can then be reduced if it is found that by so doing the distribution is not distorted.

4.2 THE FREQUENCY HISTOGRAM AND FREQUENCY POLYGON

The *frequency histogram* is a graphic display of the same information contained in the frequency table. It is a particularly useful device because it conveys the impression of the shape and pattern of a distribution at a glance. The user sees the whole picture first, then the details. In the case of the frequency table the reverse is true. The details must be studied first.

Frequency Histogram

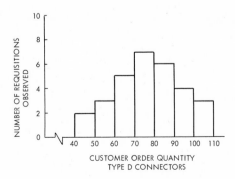

CUSTOMER ORDER QUANTITY
TYPE D CONNECTORS

Provided the vertical axis begins at zero, the area of the histogram above any interval along the horizontal axis is proportional to the number of observations within the interval. There were twice as many observations between 80 and 90 units (a total of 6) as there were between 50 and 60 (only 3); therefore it follows that the area above the former interval is twice that of the latter. Because of the significance of the areas of each class interval, the histogram conveys a properly proportioned pictorial impression—a feature lacking in most point-to-point line graphs.

A variation of the frequency histogram is the *frequency polygon*. This is a single-line graph constructed by connecting what would be the mid-points of the bars of the histogram. Below is a frequency polygon using the same data with skeleton lines included to illustrate the method of construction. The advantage of the frequency

Frequency Polygon

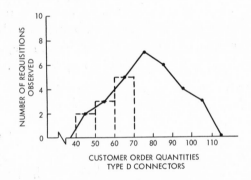

polygon lies in the fact that it is suggestive of the nature of the universe that underlies the sample from which the data is drawn. (We will return to this advantage later.)

4.3 PERCENTAGE FREQUENCY DISTRIBUTION

Sometimes it adds to understanding if *relative* rather than *absolute* frequencies are used. In the previous table absolute frequencies, the actual counts, were used. These are easily converted to relative frequencies by expressing them as a per cent of the total observations. For instance, 2 observations from a total of 30 are 2/30 or 6.7 per cent of the total. This is illustrated in the final column of the following table:

Order Quantity	Number of Observations	Per Cent Frequency of Observations
Less than 40	0	0.0%
40–50	2	6.7
50–60	3	10.0
60–70	5	16.7
70–80	7	23.3
80–90	6	20.0
90–100	4	13.3
100–110	3	10.0
110 or more	0	0.0
	30	100.0%

The same information can now be graphed in either histogram or polygon form as before using the percentage frequencies as the vertical scale instead of the absolute frequencies as was done previously. Relative frequency tables and graphs are particularly useful when two frequency distributions involving different numbers of observations are to be compared.

 13. In the box below, sketch the percentage frequency polygon for the data in the table above. Be sure to label the co-ordinates (the horizontal and vertical scales) and calibrate the scales.

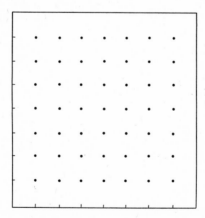

4.4 CUMULATIVE FREQUENCY DISTRIBUTION

Another useful addition to the frequency table is a column to accumulate the sum of the frequencies as indicated below:

Order Quantity	Number of Observations	Cumulative Frequency of Observations
Less than 40 0		0
40–50 2		2
50–60 3		5
60–70 5		10
etc.		

In this example the last column may appear quite foreign. Many familiar and useful business forms and reports, however, contain a very similar column labeled "total year to date." The notion of cumulative frequencies and that of cumulative totals are identical. Both are a means of recognizing that individual weeks, months, or orders are not reliable indicators of significant changes. As a result, disruptive or expensive corrective actions are delayed until a shift in the business pattern is corroborated by the total cumulative effect. In a very real sense businesses are managed, not by observations in isolation, but by the *cumulative* impact of the observations.

4.5 CUMULATIVE PERCENTAGE FREQUENCIES

Often it is desirable to show in tabular or graphic form the proportion of the observations that lie above or below a given value or range of values. *Cumulative percentage frequencies* serve this purpose.

Again using the same data the table is constructed as follows:

Order Quantity	f	% f	Cum. f	Cum. % f
Less than 40 0	0	0.0	0	0.0
40–50 2	2	6.7	2	6.7
50–60 3	3	10.0	5	16.7
60–70 5	5	16.7	10	33.3
70–80 7	7	23.3	17	56.6
80–90 6	6	20.0	23	76.6
90–100 4	4	13.3	27	90.0
100–110 3	3	10.0	30	100.0
110 or more 0	0	0.0	30	100.0
	30	100.0		

The first 3 columns are the same as in the former percentage frequency table. Two additional columns have been added and the columns have been labeled using the following conventional statistical notation:

f is frequency of observations

$\% f$ is percentage frequency

Cum. *f*   is cumulative frequency (obtained by adding the figure in the *f* column cumulatively as shown in paragraph 4.4.)

Cum. % *f*   is cumulative percentage frequency (obtained by adding the figures in the %*f* column cumulatively—or, by converting the cum. *f* column into percentages of the total of the *f* column.)

The table has the advantage of allowing proportions of orders *less than* a particular size to be read directly. For example, 100 per cent of the orders were for quantities of *less than* 110 units, 76.6 per cent of the orders were for quantities under 90 units, and only 6.7 per cent of the orders were for fewer than 50 units.

Notice that it can only be said that the cumulative percentage frequency is *less than the upper limit of the class interval.* If the mid-points were used, as in the case of the percentage frequency table and polygon, one might say, for example, that 6.7 per cent of the observations were less than 45. This we know to be inaccurate because going back to the ordered array we find only one observation less than 45, or 3.3 per cent, not 6.7 per cent. The second observation in this interval was 48 which is certainly not less than the mid-point of 45.

The cumulative percentage frequency polygon is constructed in the same manner as previously *with the exception* that now straight lines join the *upper limits* rather than the mid-points of the class intervals.

Cumulative Percentage Frequency Polygon

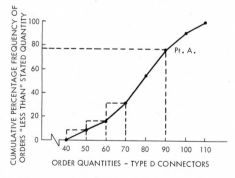

Using Point A as an example, the cumulative percentage frequency is read as follows: Approximately 75 per cent of the orders (actually 76.6 per cent as the table shows) were for less than 90 units. Reading intermediate points on the curve, of course, is subject to minor errors caused by uneven distributions within the individual class intervals; but for most practical work these errors can be neglected.

14. The following cumulative percentage frequency table has been started with the thought in mind of constructing a cumulative frequency polygon that can be read in "equal to or more than" terms rather than "less than" terms as previously illustrated.

Order Quantity	f	% f	Cum. f	Cum. % f
Less than 40	0	0.0	___	___
40–50	2	6.7	___	___
50–60	3	10.0	___	___
60–70	5	16.7	___	___
70–80	7	23.3	___	___
80–90	6	20.0	___	___
90–100	4	13.3	7	___
100–110	3	10.0	3	10.0
110 or more	0	0.0	0	0.0
	30	100.0		

Fill in the blank spaces above.

15. In the box following, sketch the cumulative percentage frequency polygon from the above data. Label and calibrate the co-ordinates.

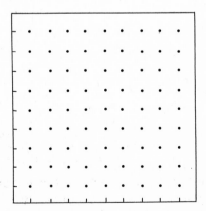

16. Values of a variable that are equal to but not greater than the upper limit of a particular class interval are, by convention, included in that interval.

True   False

4.6 BIVARIATE DATA

Thus far the methods of organizing data that have been illustrated involved *univariate* data, i.e., data in which a single variable was observed and measured. (The example used had the single variable, customer order quantities of Type D Connectors.)

To illustrate a method of organizing *bivariate data*[4] a new example is required in which there are two variables of interest. Since we are concerned here with method, not arithmetic, the simpler our example the better. How about the bunch of coins shown below? This should serve our purpose if we consider one variable to be the number of coins of each denomination and the other to be total value by denomination.

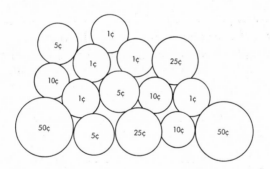

17. How many coins are there in total? _____

What is the total value of all the coins? _____

How many pennies are there? _____

What is the total value of the pennies? _____

18. In similar fashion fill in the following table. In the column marked *f* enter the number of coins by denomination. In the column marked *y* enter the total value by denomination.

---

[4] Methods of organizing bivariate data will be covered in greater detail in Chapter 5.

X	f	y
Pennies	___	___
Nickels	___	___
Dimes	___	___
Quarters	___	___
Half dollars	___	___
	15	$2.00

19. Can you expand the table to include the following additional columns?

X	f	y	Cum. f	Cum. y	Cum. % f	Cum. % y
Pennies	___	___	___	___	___	___
Nickels	___	___	___	___	___	___
Dimes	___	___	___	___	___	___
Quarters	___	___	___	___	___	___
Half dollars . . .	___	___	___	___	___	___
	15	$2.00				

Check to see if your figures agree with the points on the following graph on which the corresponding cumulative percentage frequencies of each variable have been plotted. Point A indicates, for ex-

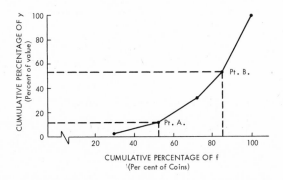

ample, that 53.3 per cent of the coins contribute only 10 per cent of the total value. This also means, of course, that the remaining 90 per cent of the value is contained in the remaining 46.7 per cent of the coins. Point B shows that 86.7 per cent of the coins contain only 50 per cent of the total value, or the other 50 per cent of the value must lie in the remaining 13.3 per cent of the coins. This illustrates quite clearly that a large per cent of the coins makes a relatively small contribution to the total value. Conversely, there is another small per cent of the coins that accounts for a rather large per cent of the total value.

This is a particularly useful polygon because it illustrates a kind of bivariate distribution often encountered in business processes. For instance, the bulk of inventory value is usually concentrated in a relatively few high-valued items. The principles of the "ABC" approach to inventory control[5] rest firmly on this common phenomenon. The phenomenon itself is often referred to as the *80–20 Rule*. The word "rule," of course, is not meant literally. The implication of the "rule" is that one frequently encounters situations in which a small per cent of one variable accounts for a large per cent of the second variable, and that relative segregations approximating 80–20 are not uncommon.

20. To test the applicability of the 80–20 Rule, fill in from your own experience your guess as to the percentages in the blank spaces below:

> 80% of the personal income tax revenue is derived from
>
> ___% of all wage earners.
>
> ___% of the total number of appropriations consume only 20% of the plant and equipment budget.
>
> 80% of the sales volume is derived from ___% of a business' customers.

21. Identify a situation in which the 80–20 Rule distribution would be of value in assigning priorities or allocating resources.

Practice Problem

The following data were obtained from stock card records at the Altoona Warehouse. The data represent stock supplied on orders for one-inch galvanized conduit during the first three months of this year.

---

[5] Items of inventory are classified (A, B, or C) according to dollar value for the purpose of exercising a degree of control commensurate with carrying costs. The "A" items are typically few in number, high in value, and receive the highest level of control.

Quantity in Feet	Number of Orders Observed
10	12
20	17
30	6
40	1
50	5
60	2
80	2
100	1
140	2
150	2
180	1
200	2
220	1
230	3
250	1
400	2
500	1
620	1
750	1
1000	1

Clerical expense is a large portion of the total operating costs of the Altoona Warehouse. Furthermore, the clerical cost of order processing is roughly the same regardless of customer order quantities. For example, it costs as much to post an inventory withdrawal of 10 feet as 1,000 feet; it costs the same to prepare an invoice for $10 as for $1,000, etc.

Using the above data construct a graph that will illustrate the fact that a large portion of the clerical effort is devoted to the processing of orders for small quantities of conduit. (Relate cumulative percentage frequency of orders to cumulative per cent of the total footage.)

Using your graph estimate the largest per cent of the total orders that account for 20 per cent of the total footage.

CHAPTER 3

Statistical Measures

1.   Averages

1.1   INTRODUCTION

Of all statistical devices *averages* are undoubtedly the best known. Baseball fans and bowlers consider themselves experts on the subject. And almost everyone else knows, or at least thinks he knows, what averages are and how they are determined.

An average is a single number used to represent a whole group (or "pile") of numerical data. It is simple, concise, and conveys some notion of the general size of the individual numbers comprising the data.

On a frequency distribution curve[1] having a bell shape like the one shown below, the average is located near the center of the distribution as shown by the arrow.

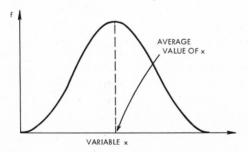

Averages describe a fundamental characteristic of a distribution

---

[1] The frequency distribution curve is similar to the frequency polygon except that it is a smooth curve. It is derived from the theoretical fact that if the sample size were extremely large and the class intervals made extremely narrow, the polygon would be indistinguishable from a smooth curve. Smooth curves are often used to depict the kind of universe presumed to underlie a particular sample.

—that is, the location or value around which the data tend to cluster or appear to balance. Hence, averages are called *measures of central tendency.*

Statisticians like to think that some skill is involved in using averages wisely, or conversely, some dangers lie in using them unwisely. The following is a case in support of their point of view:

Two months ago an acquaintance stopped in to say goodby. He considered himself quite fortunate to have been offered a job in the accounting department of a small advertising firm. After all, any company that can claim that the average accounting employee is earning $12,500 per year can certainly afford to be selective.

This week the same person stopped in again, this time just to talk. It seems that, as a result of starting in on payroll work, he had the opportunity to see the salaries of his fellow accounting department employees. Needless to say, he was a little upset to find that outside of the boss the next highest paid employee was earning only $7,000 and that employee had 15 years service. Our acquaintance suddenly had the feeling that he had—what is the expression?—"been had." He also has learned something about averages.

Assuming the company's claim was not an outright lie, you can probably guess what went wrong. The details go like this:

The Financial Vice-President, also the accounting department boss, by the way, was earning $60,000 a year. The next highest paid man received $7,000. Three others were earning $6,000; and the last three to be added to the payroll, also the balance of the accounting department employees, were each earning $5,000. Among them, the eight accounting department employees were earning $100,000—an average of $12,500 per man, just like the help-wanted ad said. The recent addition to the payroll, of course, reduced this impressive average slightly.

The point of this illustration is probably related to the reason that the word "figure," in addition to being synonymous with "compute," also means "to imagine." So it takes no talent, then, to "figure" the average salary. But this is a hard way to learn that the kind of average statisticians call the *arithmetic mean* can, at times, be worse than useless.

1. An airplane is flying a course in the shape of a square. It flies the first side at 100 mph, the second at 200 mph, the third at 300 mph, and the fourth at 400 mph. What is the average speed of the plane?

1.2 MEAN, MEDIAN, MODE

The concept of an average, while familiar, is also elusive. "Average" can mean different things to different people or to the same people at different times. To avoid using the term vaguely, statisticians have isolated different meanings of the word average and identified each with a more explicit term. For instance, to most people most of the time the word average implies what statisticians term the *arithmetic mean*. In addition to the arithmetic mean, however, there are other connotations of the word "average," each of which is also a measure of central tendency. The *median* and *mode* are two examples.

The *arithmetic mean* is only one of several kinds of mean value. Other common means are the geometric, harmonic, logarithmic, and quadratic means. We will consider only the arithmetic mean here. (The problem involving the airplane happened to be a situation in which the harmonic mean is useful, but not necessary—not necessary as long as your answer was 192 mph, that is.)

The arithmetic mean, as you no doubt know, is the sum of the observations divided by the number of observations in a particular sample. If we use x to represent the variable being studied and x_1 ("x sub 1") to represent the first observation, x_2 to represent the second, etc., and n to represent the total number of observations, we can express the formula for calculating the arithmetic mean as:

$$\bar{x} = \frac{\sum_{i=1}^{n} x_i}{n}.$$

$\bar{x}$ ("x-bar") represents the arithmetic mean.

$$\sum_{i=1}^{n} x_i$$

is read "the sum of all the x's starting with x_1 up through the last value of x or x_n" ("x-sub n" or "the nth value of x"). This is usually abbreviated to:

$$\bar{x} = \frac{\Sigma x}{n}.$$

Here, Σx is understood to mean "the sum of all x's." (Σ is the uppercase form of the Greek letter sigma.)

2. Find $\bar{x}$ for the following data: 13, 15, 20, 21, 22, 23, 24, 29, 31.

$$\bar{x} = \underline{\hspace{2cm}}.$$

The *median,* another kind of average, is determined very simply. It is the middle observation in a set of data if the data were arranged in the form of an ordered array. If the array happens to consist of an even number of observations, in which case there would be no *single* middle observation, the median may assume any number at or between the *two* middle observations. It is customary in such cases, however, to take the number mid-way between the two middle observations. In either case, odd or even, an equal number of observations lies on either side of the median. Stated more precisely, the median may be any number that neither exceeds nor is exceeded by more than half of the observations.

 3. What is the median in each of the following ordered arrays?

2, 3, 4, 5, 6   _____

2, 3, 4, 5, 63521   _____

2, 3, 4, 5, 6, 7   _____

2, 3, 4, 5, 6, 6, 7   _____

Remembering the accountant who anticipated a $12,500 salary at the advertising firm, and looking at your answers above, what measure of central tendency (average) would have been more helpful to him, the mean or the median?

4. What is the median salary in the following frequency distribution?

Weekly Earnings	f
$53.91	1
54.47	1
54.85	1
55.00	3
56.00	2
59.90	1
63.00	4
63.47	1

The mode, a third kind of average, is the value of the observation that appears most frequently in a set of data. Sometimes a set of data will exhibit more than one value around which the individual observations cluster; such distributions are termed *multimodal.* To illustrate, a *bimodal* frequency distribution curve is shown below. The arrows mark the location of the modal values.

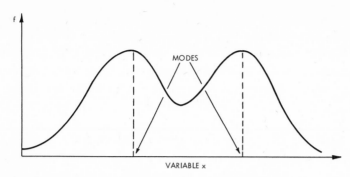

VARIABLE x

5. Indicate the modes in the following arrays.

   3, 4, 4, 4, 5, 5, 6   _____

   2, 2, 2, 3, 3, 4, 4, 4   _____

6. What is the modal salary in the weekly earnings data in exercise 4 above?

   _____

1.3 PROPERTIES OF MEANS, MEDIANS, AND MODES

The *mode* is the concept most people have in mind when they use the word "average" under the following circumstances: "The average customer buys model number SD402." In this case, the word "average" implies most popular (fashionable, *à la mode*), hence most numerous.

Using the frequency distribution curve (this time, single modal), the mode is the value of the variable corresponding to the highest point on the curve; because, by definition, this is the value occurring with the greatest frequency.

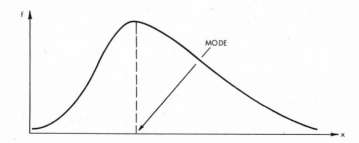

One use of the concept of the mode that may be familiar occurs in applying "critical path" or "PERT" scheduling techniques. These techniques usually require that three different estimates be made of the time required to perform a particular task. One of the three is an estimate of the "most likely" time; the others are a "pessimistic" and an "optimistic" estimate. From these estimates, an "expected value" is computed. In the computation, the "most likely" estimate is assumed to represent the modal value while the resulting "expected value" corresponds to an arithmetic mean. The formula relating these estimates is derived from a special distribution called a "beta" distribution. (Questions of uncertainty and the use of model distributions like the "beta" distribution will be discussed in a later text.)

Since the *median* depends on position within an ordered array[2] rather than the magnitude of the observations, it is a particularly appropriate average when one very large or very small value is present. For instance, in the advertising firm example, the Vice-President's salary was very high in comparison to the other salaries. As a result, the median of $6,000 is a better representation of employee salaries than the arithmetic mean. In this case the $12,500 arithmetic mean, which turns out to be a good deal more than the earnings of 7/8 of the employees, could hardly be considered representative.

The median has the property of dividing the *area* under the frequency distribution curve into two equal halves as shown below. Area A = Area B.

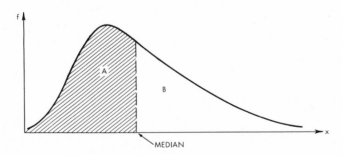

As you have seen, the *arithmetic mean* has weaknesses; but it also has unique advantages not shared by the median or mode. For instance:

---

[2] Because its value is determined from the *ordered* array, the median is sometimes referred to as an *order statistic*. *Percentiles* which, in effect, divide the total frequency into one hundred equal parts rather than just two are other examples of *order statistics*.

It takes into consideration the value of each individual observation.

It can be determined conveniently without first arranging the data in the form of an ordered array.

It can have one, and only one, value for a given set of data.

It is particularly excellent for further numerical calculations.

This last advantage requires further explanation. The nature of the numerical advantage of the arithmetic mean lies in the property that the algebraic sum[3] of the differences between each observation and the mean is always zero. This can be illustrated as follows:

Given the following observations: 12, 23, 30, 39, and 46, the arithmetic mean is:

$$\bar{x} = \frac{\Sigma x}{n} = \frac{12 + 23 + 30 + 39 + 46}{5} = 30.$$

The individual differences from the mean, called "deviations," are shown in the column labeled $(x_i - \bar{x})$.

x_i	$\bar{x}$	$x_i - \bar{x}$
12	30	−18
23	30	− 7
30	30	0
39	30	+ 9
46	30	+16

From this table it can be seen that the algebraic sum of the deviations is 0, i.e.:

$$\Sigma (x_i - \bar{x}) = 0.$$

In effect, the arithmetic mean sacrifices the desire to be typical or representative in the same sense that the median is representative, in favor of the numerical advantage illustrated above. This advantage will be useful in considering variability later in this chapter.

On the same frequency distribution curves as shown below, it can be seen that the mean, median, and mode will coincide only in the special case of a symmetrical distribution. In other cases, however, the values do not coincide as shown in the lopsided (or *skewed*) distribution on the right.

---

[3] The algebraic sum means that attention must be paid to the sign when adding. For example, the algebraic sum of −2, −3, and +1 is a −4.

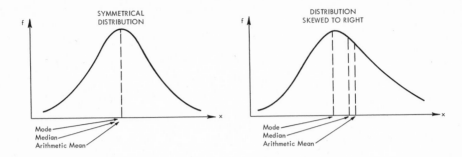

7. In the following statement, the word "average" could be intended as either the arithmetic mean, the median, or the
mode: "The average starting salary is $500/month." Very
briefly explain the meaning of the statement if "average" were
interpreted:

As the arithmetic mean. _____

_____

As the median. _____

_____

As the mode. _____

_____

2.   Variability

2.1   THE E. R. MONROE CASE

The E. R. Monroe Co. is a well-established, medium-sized, manufacturing firm. Its sales figures have run about $14 million and its
employment level has stayed pretty close to 950 for the last five
years. Except for its line of packaging products, some of which are
sold to drug and cosmetic firms, and a line of precision stampings
for military customers, most of its sales are concentrated in the
jewelry industry. Monroe's income last year was $560,000. They
have always enjoyed a reputation for being a stable and reliable
vendor and have generally been regarded as one of the best-
managed firms of their size in the jewelry industry.

With few exceptions Monroe's direct labor force, numbering
about 700, is represented by the JWI, the jewelry workers' union.
It is the practice in this industry, as you may already know, to
negotiate employee *benefits* on a company-wide basis, but to nego-

tiate *wages* for each class of work in a shop separately. This wage negotiation practice dates back to the days when two products of the same design sold for different prices depending on the skill of the individual artisan. For years, however, this antiquated practice has been little more than a ritual. Supposedly, the system gives a lot of people "a chance to be heard"; but the fact is, the wage settlement in the first shop group invariably sets the pattern for all other groups within a particular company.

The Standard Fastener Line at Monroe was the key group in last year's negotiations. Being first in line meant that the settlement in Standard Fasteners would write the ticket for Monroe that year.

Fred Miller was foreman of the Standard Fastener Line. There are many variations of standard fasteners and Fred's biggest job was to see that they got produced in the right mix. The work involved in making the fasteners was about the same regardless of the particular variety. That is to say, it was a straight piecework operation and the standard price was 30 cents per fastener regardless of variety. The work itself, while mainly of an assembly nature, was quite intricate and required a high degree of skill.

Last year's negotiations got off to the usual start, i.e., with a lengthy complaint from the union about piece prices in general. It did not take long, however, for this first meeting to take an unexpected twist. Here is the gist of the union's demand relative to the Standard Fastener Line extracted from the recorded minutes of the meeting:

Our stand is simple so we'll get right to the point. 30 cents a unit is ridiculous. . . . A fair price in our opinion is 31½ cents.

The men average about 94 units/day.[4] Therefore, the cent and a half more that we're requesting amounts to an average of $1.41 more per man.

. . . You know yourself that this is the smallest increase we've ever demanded.

Make no mistake about it, we are not playing a game. 31½ cents is *it*. . . . If you have any doubts about our intentions, just try us.

The union's strategy in this meeting was a real surprise. In the past the union's first demand was purposely out of line and neither side took it very seriously. This time their demand was in the same ball park, at least dollarwise, with the kind of offer that Monroe's

---

[4] As a result of a former bonus system, it was a long-standing custom in the shop to reckon output on an average daily basis. Although each man's output was, and still is in fact, tallied daily, the bonus was paid on daily output averaged over the week. The theory was that this gave a man a better chance to recoup if he happened to have one or two bad days.

management was contemplating. Furthermore, the demand was in the form of a "this or nothing" ultimatum—and right off the bat.

At their first meeting following the session with the union, Monroe's management heard the following points made by the Cost Analyst:

1. The union's figure of 94 units per day per man checks out all right. I checked their figure using the latest Production Summary Report.[5] It works out like this:

$$\frac{7,990 \,^{①}}{5} = 1,598 \text{ units/day,}$$

$$\frac{1,598}{17 \,^{②}} = 94 \text{ units/day/man.}$$

2. The average weekly cost then is $2,516.85:
$$7,990 \,(.315) = 2,516.85.$$

3. Our current cost on the same basis is $2,397.00:
$$7,990 \,(.30) = 2,397.00$$

4. The additional direct labor in cost center 172,[③] alone, is $119.85 per week. Annualized this is just about $6,000 per year.

$$\begin{array}{r} 2,516.85 \\ 2,397.00 \\ \hline 119.85 \end{array}$$

$$119.85 \,(50) = 5,992.50.$$

5. This amounts to a 5% increase.
$$\frac{119.85}{2,397.00} \,(100) = 5\%.$$

6. Direct labor at current rates is estimated at $3.85 million. Assuming a 5 per cent increase across the board, which, of course, is what we have to anticipate, total direct labor would increase $192,500 a year.
$$3,850,000 \,(.05) = 192,500.$$

			PRODUCTION			
			SUMMARY REPORT			
			FISCAL WEEK 10			
COST CNTR	FOREMAN	UNIT OUTPUT THIS WEEK	TOTL OUTPT YTD	AVG WKLY OUTPT YTD	PERF FACTOR THIS WEEK	AVG WKLY DIR HRLY EMP YTD
172 ③	MILLER	8020	79900	7990 ①	+3.4	17.0 ②

---

[5] Numbers in circles above figures are keyed to the report.

Prior to the negotiations management had concluded that 3 per cent would be a reasonable offer. They felt this was roughly the rate at which shop productivity had been increasing in recent years. The details of this offer had been fully worked out, by the way. Privately, however, they had set 4 1/2 per cent as the upper limit not to be exceeded under any conditions. And even at that they felt some scheme would have to be included which would act as a positive incentive to increase productivity. Up to this point not much thought had been given to exactly how this might be accomplished. As a result of the union's surprise strategy, however, Monroe's negotiating team decided not to hesitate any longer. Working late that evening, they put together what they called their "upper limit" package using the 4 1/2 per cent criteria. The salient points of the resulting plan were as follows:

1. Maintain the 30 cent per unit standard price but provide a bonus of 14 cents for each unit over a daily average of 85 units/man.[6]

2. Since the average output per day per man is 94, that means that on the average we will pay for 9 bonus units per man per day.

3. The projected weekly cost then is $2,504.10:
$$94 \ (.30) + 9 \ (.14) = 29.46,$$
$$29.46 \ (5)(17) = 2,504.10.$$

4. This amounts to an average increase of $107.10 per week or slightly under the 4½ per cent upper limit.

$$\begin{array}{r} 2,504.10 \\ \underline{2,397.00} \\ 107.10 \end{array}$$

$$\frac{107.10}{2,397.00} \ (100) = 4.47\%.$$

5. Furthermore this plan offers the following additional advantages: Right away the average guy gets 9 bonus units. This should make the plan appear quite attractive.

Since the output does not vary much from week to week,[7] and since the greatest room for improvement will come from those individuals who are currently below average, we can expect the largest portion of any increase in production to come from units at the lower cost

---

[6] A former bonus system was similar in nature. The former system provided an incentive all right but it was a failure because the job rates were poorly established in the first place. Since then, however, the Industrial Engineering group had corrected pretty nearly all of the rate problems through use of vastly improved motion and time study techniques.

[7] This was obvious from the weekly Production Summary Reports.

of 30 cents each. Those currently above average probably cannot improve very much. To the extent that this occurs, of course, there is a tendency to reduce the average cost below the 31 1/3 cents per unit that would result if no change at all occurs.

$$\frac{29.46}{94} = \$.3133/\text{unit.}$$

At this point management had an important strategy decision to make. Should they play all their cards at once as the union appeared to do, or should they go ahead as originally planned with the 3 per cent offer? Two questions were worthy of further consideration.

1. How good were the rates?
2. And could they really anticipate a productivity increase as suggested by the 4½ percent offer plan?

Fred Miller, the foreman, was called into the meeting and offered the following additional information on these two points:

1. Oh, a few guys could improve their own average a little but by and large the average daily outputs aren't going to change much for long. The rates are just too tight for any significant movement.
2. This doesn't mean that the men all operate at the same level, but individually they all work pretty close to their own maximum capabilities.
3. A number of the men do average under 85 units per day. Of the few who could show a sustained improvement, most of them will be in this less-than-85 category.

Fred's inputs clinched it. With some reservations but with the hope of an early settlement, Monroe decided to go into the meeting with their best offer—the 4 1/2 per cent "upper limit" plan.

The following day the offer was made. The union indicated that they did not fully understand it and wanted a recess to review it before, in their words, "we reject it." The next meeting was set for the following afternoon.

In the morning of the following day Fred Miller reported that his Production Performance Report[8] was missing. He did not know who "stole" it, but he was willing to bet the union steward had it.

The next meeting with the union lasted only a few minutes. The

---

[8] This is a tab run provided to the foreman as a measure of individual and group efficiency. It is considered confidential since individual earnings can easily be determined from it.

union's counsel began by explaining management's offer in his words, "just to be certain that I understand it." After being assured that he had stated the details correctly, he announced that the union approved the plan and intended to recommend its acceptance to its membership. He also added that he expected this to serve as the basis for settlement in the other units as usual and that the whole wage matter, in his opinion, could probably be completed in record time.

And that was that. *Or was it?* Some gnawing questions remained in the minds of Monroe's negotiating team. Why had the union been so quick to agree? What was that business of Miller's Production Performance Report all about? Was there any connection between these two questions? While they were still puzzling over these questions, the phone rang. It was Miller. "Don't worry about that Production Performance Report. The boys apparently swiped it to do a little figuring, but it's back again," Miller announced. Just to pursue these questions a little further in hope of satisfying their curiosity, the negotiating team asked Miller to bring the report down to the office.

The tab run, just as Miller presented it, is shown on the next page. Miller explained that the handwritten figures were added by whoever took the report the night before.

"Hey, wait a minute. Let me see that thing again," cried Joe Becker, the Cost Analyst. After a few pencil scratches Becker came out with a loud, "Oh, no!" With this he went to the flip chart and showed the following computations.

$$1598^{(4)}(.30) + 210^{(5)}(.14) = 508.80/\text{day}$$
$$508.80 (5) = 2,544.00/\text{wk}.$$

$$\begin{array}{r} 2,544.00 \\ 2,397.00 \\ \hline 147.00 \text{ additional} \end{array}$$

$$\frac{147.00}{2,397.00}(100) = 6.18\%$$

"Gentlemen, what this means is that while the union was looking for an increase of 5% and we thought we were offering them 4½%, we really gave them 6.2%. And what's worse, they know it."

Think it's unbelievable, couldn't happen? Ask anyone in the jewelry industry what their opinion of E. R. Monroe is now. They will undoubtedly mention Monroe's "give away program" of last year. The whole industry is trying to recover from that prize package.

PRODUCTION PERFORMANCE
REPORT

FISCAL WEEK – 10

COST CENTER – 172

FOREMAN – MILLER

EMPLOYEE PAY NO.	AVG. DAILY OUTPUT THIS WEEK	AVG. DAILY OUTPUT Y – T – D	
1390	114	120	3⟨
1427	75	73	0
1492	116	118	33
1526	82	80	0
1532	75	78	0
1607	107	107	22
1692	119	122	3⟨
1711	87	78	0
1718	84	83	0
1763	70	76	0
1848	97	93	8
1877	124	123	38
1946	81	85	0
1993	119	110	25
2020	75	71	0
2105	97	97	12
2125	82	84	0 ⑤ ─── 2⟨0

TOTAL OUTPUT THIS WEEK – 8020

TOTAL YEAR TO DATE   – 79900

AVG. DAILY THIS WEEK   – 1604

AVG. DAILY YEAR TO DATE – 1598 ④

PERFORMANCE FACTOR THIS WEEK – +.734

2.2 WHAT WENT WRONG AT MONROE?

In computing the cost of their wage offer Monroe used a figure of 94 units per day per man. This was the average, or more precisely the arithmetic mean, of the set of data involved. On recomputing the cost of their wage offer using the actual data rather than the mean, however, the results proved to be quite different. The difference lies in the fact that use of the arithmetic mean contained a hidden assumption—hidden at least to Monroe's management. While it is true that on the average the men were producing 9 bonus units each (the difference between 94 and 85), using this fact as Monroe had in computing total direct labor cost assumes that each man averaging *under* 85 units per day would pay *back* to the company 14 cents for each unit between his average output and 85 units. This, of course, was not a part of the wage offer at all. Monroe had fallen into a "better than average" sized trap.

The Monroe case is a situation in which the arithmetic mean did not reveal enough information about the data. Had either the median or the mode been used in place of the arithmetic mean, Monroe would have been in even more serious trouble. None of these figures, in fact, reveal any information regarding the way that the data are dispersed or scattered about the average; and this, of course, was the key to the problem.

Regardless of the average used, data are typically dispersed about that average in some fashion. This, in fact, is the reason for computing an average in the first place: to see through the variability to a central location. *Variability* or dispersion, however, is a characteristic of data that is often equally as important as the tendency for the data to concentrate at or around a particular central value. It is obvious, for instance, that if you could not swim you would be ill-advised to attempt to wade across a river knowing only that it had a mean depth of two feet. Additional information about the river's depth is clearly essential. So was additional information essential at Monroe, but at Monroe the need was not so obvious. Figuratively speaking, the water was over their heads a few feet from shore.

In the Monroe case the number of observations was small so the variability of the data was eventually taken into account by considering each observation separately. Where large amounts of data are involved, however, this is impractical. Instead this characteristic is summarized through *measures of variability* just as averages are used to summarize the characteristics of central tendency. Measures of variability in effect complement averages. The reason for this can be seen more clearly from the following two frequency distribution curves shown. Distributions A and B are quite different, yet they both have the same arithmetic mean. The difference lies in the fact that Distribution B has the greater variability.

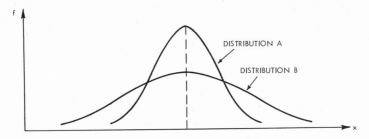

8. It takes an average (arithmetic mean) of 16 hours to process the payroll. Assuming that the payroll must be ready for disbursal at 8:00 A.M. Friday morning, when must you start the processing to finish on time? (Assume a single shift operation.)

    Circle One

    Monday morning

    No later than 8:00 A.M. Wednesday morning

    Insufficient data in problem

9. How long will it be before your inventory of Dingus Contraptions is depleted, if your beginning inventory is five, the monthly production rate is four, and you sell an average (median) of six contraptions per month?

    Less than two months

    Insufficient data in problem

    2 5/6 months

10. The average employment in your company was 6,540 people two years ago. Last year employment averaged 6,550 people. (Both averages are 13-point mean values.) This shows that employment in the company was relatively stable during this two-year period.   T   or   F?

2.3 THE RANGE

The simplest measure of variability to compute is the *range*. The range is the amount of variation exhibited between the two extreme valued observations. This can be determined directly from an ordered array by subtracting the smallest value of the variable, one end of the array, from the largest, the other end of the array.

The ease with which the range can be determined, however, is offset by its limitations. Since it is solely dependent on extreme values of the variable, it does not reflect the distribution of observations between the extremes. For example, consider the two cases below:

Case I 10, 14, 18, 22, 26, 30, 34
Case II 10, 19, 21, 22, 23, 25, 34

In both cases the arithmetic mean is 22 and the range is 24. In Case I, however, the data is uniformly distributed between 10 and 34, while in Case II most of the values cluster closely about the mean. For this reason the range is a poor descriptive measure[9] for comparing sets of data.

The financial pages of the newspapers are one of the few places where the range is still used extensively as a descriptive measure. The range of the *New York Times* 50 Stock Average, for instance, appears daily in graphic form. Also, the equivalent to the range is provided by quoting the high and low prices at which each listed stock has been traded during the year. The danger in this practice, of course, is that any unusual variation in price at any time in the year leaves a lasting and possibly erroneous impression of a particular stock's volatility.

2.4 ORDER STATISTICS AS MEASURES OF VARIABILITY

The median, you recall, was referred to as an *order statistic* because its value was determined by position within the ordered array. Since as many observations lie above as below the median, it is sometimes referred to as the *50th percentile*. Any number of similar order statistics or percentiles can also be determined. In fact, it is possible to reproduce the original data by determining a sufficient number of percentiles.

Measures of variability may be obtained by taking the difference between two percentiles that are equidistant from the median. The 10th and 90th percentiles are commonly used for this purpose. The resulting measure of variability, in this case, is called the *decile range*. (The 90th percentile is the value at or below which 90 per cent of the observations lie. Likewise, the 10th percentile is the value at or below which 10 per cent of the observations lie.) If the value of the 10th percentile were $1,250, for instance, and the value of the 90th percentile were $2,400, then the decile range would be $1,150; i.e., 2,400 − 1,250 = 1,150. This reveals that the central 80 per cent of the observations all lie within a span of $1,150.

---

[9] The range is considerably more useful in problems of statistical inference involving small samples than it is as a descriptive measure of variability.

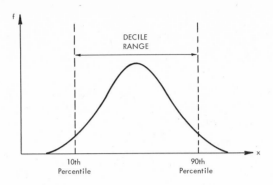

Perhaps you recall that, given an even number of observations, no single one of them, strictly speaking, represents the median. In order to arrive at a precise (i.e., repeatable) value for the median in such cases it was necessary to adopt a convention, namely that we will take as the median a value lying midway between the two middle observations. When dealing with percentiles we must, for the same reason, adopt a similar convention. For instance, in the following data, strictly speaking, there is no 75th percentile:

$$350, \quad 394, \quad 423, \quad 446, \quad 455, \quad 489, \quad 505.$$

Since there are seven observations, the 75th percentile (also called the *third quartile*) occurs at the 5.25th observation; but, of course, there is no such observation. In such cases the 75th percentile is approximated by adding .25 of the difference between the 5th and 6th observation to the 5th observation as shown below:

$$\text{75th percentile}[10] = 455 + .25(489 - 455) = 463.5.$$

Order statistics effectively eliminate the influence of extreme values, therefore their use is generally more satisfactory for measuring variability than the range. They are, however, subject to the same limitation as the median. That is, since the value of every observation is not taken into account in their determination, further mathematical treatment of order statistics is limited.

---

[10] The difference between per cents and percentiles is often confusing. Using the example above, the *75th percentile* is the value of the variable (463.5) at the boundary between the first 75 per cent and the last 25 per cent of the observations. The first 75 *per cent* may have reference to either the group of observations between 350 and 463.5 or the range of the variable between these limits or both, but not to the value of the variable at the boundary.

2.5 THE STANDARD DEVIATION

It is not exactly obvious to most of us that the square root of the mean of the squared deviations of a set of numbers about its arithmetic mean makes an excellent measure of variability. But it does, and it is called the *standard deviation*. This is one drawback of the standard deviation: it does not have an intuitively obvious meaning. The statistician, fortunately, has more faith in his mathematics than in his intuition, with the result that this measure is the most common and certainly the most satisfactory of all the measures of variability. The concept of the standard deviation, in fact, is one of the most important in modern statistics.

To see what the standard deviation really is, let us go back to that first sentence again and try to decipher it. We know what the arithmetic mean is, so we can start there. You may also recall that the sum of the deviations (i.e., the differences from the mean to each individual value in a set of data) equaled zero. We can write this as:

$$\Sigma(x - \bar{x}) = 0.$$

The algebraic sum of the deviations about the arithmetic mean is *always* zero.

A second mathematical characteristic of the arithmetic mean is that the sum of the squares of the deviations about the arithmetic mean is a minimum. That is, the sum of the squares of the deviations about the mean are less than they would be about any value other than the mean. Symbolically, the sum of the squared deviations about the mean is:

$$\Sigma(x - \bar{x})^2.$$

To find the arithmetic mean of the sum of the squared deviations, we simply divide by n—where n is the number of x's—as follows:

$$\frac{1}{n}\Sigma(x - \bar{x})^2.$$

At this point we have written a formula for the *variance*.[11] The usual symbol for the variance is s^2, hence:

---

[11] The statistical use of the word *variance*, as you can see, is quite different from the familiar nontechnical use of the word.

$$s^2 = \frac{1}{n}\Sigma(x - \overline{x})^2.$$

Since the standard deviation is defined as the square root of the variance, the equation for the *standard deviation* is:

$$s = \sqrt{s^2} = \sqrt{\frac{1}{n}\Sigma(x - \overline{x})^2}.$$

The equation above is in a form that is probably easiest to remember; but in order to compute s, it is more convenient to use a slightly different formula, which can be derived by algebraic manipulation and basic definitions:

$$s = \frac{1}{n}\sqrt{n\Sigma(x^2) - (\Sigma x)^2}.$$

Using this last form, we can compute s without first computing the mean, $\overline{x}$, or any of the actual deviations from the mean.

To illustrate the two equivalent formulas, let us compute s in two ways for the data comprised of the six observations below:

$$0, \quad 1, \quad 3, \quad 4, \quad 4, \quad 6$$

Using the definition formula:

$$s = \sqrt{\frac{1}{n}\Sigma(x - \overline{x})^2}$$

x		$x - \overline{x}$	$(x - \overline{x})^2$
0	$\overline{x} = \dfrac{1}{n}\Sigma x$	− 3	9
1		− 2	4
3	$= \dfrac{1}{6}(18) = 3$	0	0
4		+ 1	1
4		+ 1	1
6		+ 3	9
$\Sigma x = 18$		$\Sigma(x - \overline{x}) = 0$	$\Sigma(x - \overline{x})^2 = 24$

$$s = \sqrt{\frac{1}{n}\Sigma(x - \overline{x})^2}$$

$$= \sqrt{\frac{1}{6}\Sigma(x - \overline{x})^2}$$

$$= \sqrt{\frac{1}{6}(24)}$$

$$= \sqrt{4}$$

$$s = 2$$

Using the computational formula:

$$s = \frac{1}{n}\sqrt{n\Sigma(x^2) - (\Sigma x)^2}$$

x	x^2
0	0
1	1
3	9
4	16
4	16
6	36
$\Sigma x = 18$	$\Sigma(x^2) = 78$

$$s = \frac{1}{6}\sqrt{6(78) - (18)^2}$$

$$= \frac{1}{6}\sqrt{468 - 324}$$

$$= \frac{1}{6}\sqrt{144} = \frac{12}{6} = 2$$

For manual computations with small amounts of data, the first method is satisfactory; but for long computations, either with a desk calculator or a computer, the second method is much easier.

11. The statement was made, but without proof, that the sum of the squared deviations about the arithmetic mean is less than about any other value.

The sum of the squared deviations about the mean in the following data is as shown:

x	$x - \bar{x}$	$(x - \bar{x})^2$
1	-3	9
2	-2	4
3	-1	1
4	0	0
5	$+1$	1
6	$+2$	4
7	$+3$	9
	$\Sigma(x - \bar{x}) = 0$	$\Sigma(x - \bar{x})^2 = 28$

Test the statement regarding the minimum sum of squares by taking deviations about some value (call it x') other than the mean. Use the following table:

x	$x - x'$	$(x - x')^2$
1		
2		
3		
4		
5		
6		
7		

	Circle One
Is $\Sigma(x - x')$ still zero?	Yes No
Is $\Sigma(x - x')^2$ larger or smaller than before?	Larger Smaller

2.6 PROPERTIES OF THE STANDARD DEVIATION

The standard deviation is a useful descriptive measure of variability for judging the representativeness of the arithmetic mean. If s is small, the data has a high degree of uniformity; if s is large, the opposite is true. Hence, if two sets of data with identical arithmetic means are compared, the data with the smaller standard deviation has the least variability (or the most representative arithmetic mean.)

In determining s, note that all the information in a set of data is used. This was not the case in determining the range or the percentile-based measures of variability. For this reason, the standard deviation has certain definite mathematical properties which, like the arithmetic mean, make it adaptable to further mathematical use. The most important of these uses results from the relationship between the standard deviation and a theoretical distribution model known as the *normal distribution*. The normal distribution is represented graphically by the familiar, smooth, and symmetrical bell-shaped curve.

The importance of the bell-shaped or *normal curve* lies in the fact that many natural phenomena follow this pattern of variation. More important, however, is the fact that many descriptive measures taken from sample data also tend to be normally distributed even though the universe from which the samples are drawn is not itself a normal distribution. This fact makes the normal distribution of fundamental importance in statistical inference and sampling theory. This will be discussed at greater length when these topics are considered. At the moment, however, we will consider the normal distribution briefly for the purpose of illustrating the relationship between this distribution and the standard deviation.

The normal distribution in graphic form (called the *normal curve*) is shown below. Since the normal curve is a model of a statistical universe, the symbols $\overline{X}$ and σ are used to represent the arithmetic mean and the standard deviation, respectively. These symbols are customarily used instead of $\overline{x}$ and s when referring to the characteristics or *parameters* of a universe.

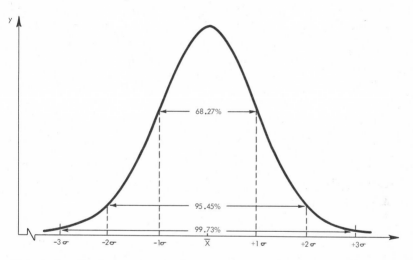

From the diagram, it can be seen that equal plus and minus deviations around the arithmetic mean include precise portions of the number of elementary units in a normally distributed universe. For instance, 68.27 per cent of the elementary units in the universe are located within one standard deviation on either side of the arithmetic mean. Likewise, 95.45 per cent of the elementary units fall within two standard deviations from the mean. The normal distribution, in fact, is completely defined by just two values: the arithmetic mean and the standard deviation.

To return to the standard deviation (s) of a set of data, as long as the distribution of the data resembles a normal distribution, the standard deviation provides a means of estimating the percentages of observations included by given distances from the mean. Hence, the following relationships can be expected to hold:

> About 68% of the observations fall within $\bar{x} \pm s$
> " 95% " " " " " $\bar{x} \pm 2s$
> " 99% " " " " " $\bar{x} \pm 3s$

This property of the standard deviation makes it useful for prediction purposes. (The question of the reliability of such predictions depends on sample size and other matters more properly considered under the heading of statistical inference.)

12. For every 10,000 elementary units in a normally distributed universe, how many would fall beyond $\bar{X} \pm 3\sigma$? (See graph.)

13. What percentage of the elementary units in a normally distributed universe would fall between $\bar{X} - 2\sigma$ and $\bar{X} + 1\sigma$?

2.7 OTHER MEASURES INVOLVING THE STANDARD DEVIATION

It was stated earlier that the standard deviation could be used to compare the variability of two sets of data provided both sets had the same arithmetic mean. Since instances of two distributions having the same mean are rare, some other way of comparing variabilities is required. This problem can be solved by expressing the standard deviation of each set of data in terms relative to its arithmetic mean. The resulting ratio, called the *coefficient of variation*, is expressed as follows:

$$V = \frac{s}{\bar{x}}.$$

The following example illustrates a use of the coefficient of variation:

The mean of the weekly shipments last year from Factory A was 220 units and the standard deviation was 31. The mean of the weekly shipments from Factory B was 340 units and the standard deviation was 41. In which factory was the week-to-week variability the greater?

In Factory A the standard deviation was 14% of its mean.

$$V = \frac{s}{\bar{x}} = \frac{31}{220} = .14.$$

In Factory B the standard deviation was only 12% of its mean.

$$V = \frac{s}{\bar{x}} = \frac{41}{340} = .12.$$

The variability, therefore, was relatively greater at Factory A.

Another useful measure is called the *standard measure* or *z-value*,

$$z = \frac{x - \bar{x}}{s}.$$

This relationship can be used to convert individual observations into units expressible in terms of the standard deviation. Using the *z value*, comparisons may be made between individual observations from different sets of data. For example, suppose we wished to compare the relative performance between the two factories of the last example based on shipments in a particular week. During the week in question, assume the shipments were 290 units from Factory A and 388 from Factory B.

For Factory A:

$$z = \frac{x - \bar{x}}{s} = \frac{290 - 220}{31} = 2.3.$$

At Factory A, then, the shipments for the week in question were 2.3 standard deviations above their mean.

For Factory B:

$$z = \frac{x - \bar{x}}{s} = \frac{388 - 340}{41} = 1.2.$$

At Factory B the shipments were only 1.2 standard deviations above their mean.

Relatively speaking, then, Factory A had a much better week than Factory B.

14. The year before last the mean monthly employment was 4,800 with a standard deviation of 300. Last year the mean monthly employment was 5,200 with a standard deviation of 360. In which year was employment relatively more stable?

Circle One

Year before last.

Last year.

15. Which of the following measures did you use above?

Circle One

Decile range

Standard measure

Coefficient of variation

Practice Problems

PROBLEM I

In the course of a study of plating operations you have been working very closely with the Manager of Shop Operations. One of the bits of data of interest is the time required to plate 100 pieces of drwg. no. 173D207. The MSO (an old Quality Control man, by the way) just dropped off the data with the request that you prepare a "statistical description" of it while he goes over to Purchasing to get some data on the purchase price of the cadmium salts used in the plating process. The data in hours is as follows:

6.25, 7.70, 7.20, 5.80, 7.35, 6.65, 7.30, 7.85,
5.50, 6.50, 7.00, 8.50, 8.15, 7.05, 6.20, 7.15,
6.55, 7.55, 7.60, 6.85, 7.00, 6.60, 7.50, 6.45,
6.75

Draw a frequency histogram.

Compute the arithmetic mean and standard deviation.

Mark the histogram to indicate $\bar{x} \pm 2s$.

PROBLEM II

There are 20 girls in the accounting office and their jobs involve checking and posting information from vouchers received from the factory floor. The arithmetic mean of the number of vouchers cleared per girl per day is 240, with a standard deviation of 30 vouchers. The distribution is approximately normal. What is your best estimate of the following:

1. The total number of vouchers cleared by all the girls each day.

2. The number of girls who clear more than 240 per day.

3. The number of girls who clear 300 vouchers or more each day.

4. The number of girls who clear less than 210 per day.

CHAPTER 4

Review of Algebra

1.   Introduction

1.1   ALGEBRA AND THE MAN IN THE STREET

No doubt you are aware of the fact
that the formula about the circle
$[C = 2\pi R]$ is
"Algebra."
And perhaps you can guess from this
that one way in which
Algebra is different from Arithmetic
is:
Whereas in Arithmetic we do
one specific problem at a time,
in ALGEBRA we give
a GENERAL rule for doing many
problems of a certain type.
Thus when we find
the area of a rectangle
whose base is 4 in. and altitude 2 in.
and get 8 square in.,
THIS IS ARITHMETIC.
But when we write
$(1)\ A = ab$
which says that
to find the area, A,
of ANY rectangle,
we must multiply the altitude, a,
by the base, b,
THIS IS ALGEBRA.

In other words,
Algebra is more GENERAL

than Arithmetic.
But perhaps you will say that
this is not much of a difference—
since in Arithmetic
we also have general rules,
but they are given in WORDS,
instead of LETTERS as in (1).
Thus in Arithmetic we would say:
"To find the area of any rectangle
multiply its altitude by its base,"
whereas in Algebra we say:

$$A = ab,$$

but, after all, you may feel that
this is merely a matter of
a convenient shorthand
rather than anything radically new.
Now the fact is that
it is not merely a question of
a convenient shorthand,
but
by writing formulas in this
very convenient symbolism—
especially when a formula is
much more complicated than
the one given above—
we are able to tell
AT A GLANCE
many interesting facts
which would be very difficult to
dig out from a complicated
statement in words.
And, furthermore,
when we learn to handle
the formulas,
we find that
we are able to solve problems
almost automatically
which would otherwise require
a great deal of hard thinking.

.   .   .

Perhaps you will say

.   .   .

"I like to talk,
I don't want to use
abstract symbols all the time!"
To which the answer is:
By all means enjoy yourself

.   .   .

but when you have a hard job to do,
be sure to avail yourself
of all possible tools,
for otherwise
you may find it impossible
to do at all.

And so,
if you wish to be an engineer
and build bridges and things,
you must know Mathematics.
If you wish to figure out
how much money to put away now
so you may have
a comfortable income in your old age,
use a formula.

If you want to know
how much interest
you are REALLY paying
when you borrow money or
when you buy things on installments,
use a formula.
And, mind you, these are
algebraic formulas:
some of these problems
CANNOT be solved by using
Arithmetic alone![1]

The above quotation appeared over twenty years ago in one of the most unusual and thoroughly original books ever written about mathematics. The quotation is included here for several reasons. First, it is a very simple but excellent description of algebra. Algebra

---

[1] H. G. and L. R. Lieber, *The Education of T. C. Mits* (Rev. ed.; New York: W. W. Norton & Co., Inc., 1942, 1944), pp. 43-47. Published in England by George Allen & Unwin Ltd.

is important because it is useful; it is different and to some extent unnatural because it involves generalizations and abstractions (symbols).

Another reason for including this quotation relates to the book itself. The title of the book is *The Education of T. C. Mits*. T. C. Mits very closely resembles you and me and most people we know. In fact, T. C. Mits is an acronym for "*The Celebrated Man In The Street*." But the man in the street already knows something about algebra, does he not? T. C. Mits *did* but he forgot most of what he learned because he never used it. This is as true of the T. C. Mits of today as it was twenty years ago. But will it be true of the T. C. Mits of ten years hence? There are good reasons for thinking that things may be changing in this respect.

1.2 THE PROBLEM OF T.C. MITS

Samuel Taylor Coleridge expressed the underlying spirit of several centuries of algebra in the following words: "Some people contend that algebra ought to be taught by making illustrations obvious to the senses. Nothing can be more absurd or injurious: it ought to be our never-ceasing effort to make people think, not feel." A surprising statement for a poet, but perhaps this explains why Coleridge is remembered as a poet, not as a mathematician.

Unfortunately, because of the "teach 'em to think" school of which Coleridge was one of many proponents, many of us never really learned to *use* algebra, at least not while studying algebra. The occasional "word problem" we encountered provided only a brief glimpse of how the concepts of algebra could be related to reality; but, even then, many of these had the trappings of riddles, not reality. (So John *is* twice as old as Mary was two years ago, etc. So what!)

On the whole, the emphasis was placed on learning the manipulative *rules* of algebra; and the important part of algebra, its use, was neglected. While simply learning this set of rules helped to solve examination problems, it did not help much when the course was over. In fact, as soon as one realized that the world was not saturated with polynomials awaiting factoring, the rules were quickly forgotten or relegated to an inactive duty status. And this is why T. C. Mits is in the same boat today as he was twenty years ago.

1.3 SOME POINTS TO KEEP IN MIND

In this chapter we will review the important rules of algebra, but since much of the value of such a review is necessarily submerged in the process, it is worthwhile to bear in mind a couple of points regarding practical usefulness.

The first point is that the set of review exercises in this chapter might appear to be unnecessarily complicated—far more complicated, in fact, than anything apt to be encountered in the practical world of business. This reaction will be especially typical of those whose previous encounters with mathematics date back a few years. Actually the opposite is true; the exercises are trivial in comparison to much of the mathematics being applied to business problems today. The reason is that many real business problems are far more complex than these exercises. Some of the problems, of course, are beyond the analytic capabilities of even the most powerful mathematical techniques.

As we begin using the symbols of algebra in the process of our review, the matter of where the symbols come from or why they are important is easily forgotten. This raises the second point: in using the symbols it is well to remember that in addition to their obvious compactness and brevity, each symbol has, or can have, a precise meaning. As a result, algebraic statements are clear and unambiguous—a necessary adjunct to exact reasoning. Contrast this with English in the following verbal exchange highlighting possible ambiguities:

From the Minutes of a Borough Council Meeting:

Councilor Trafford took exception to the proposed notice at the entrance of South Park: "No dogs must be brought to this Park except on a lead." He pointed out that this order would not prevent an owner from releasing his pets, or pet, from a lead when once safely inside the Park.

THE CHAIRMAN (COLONEL VINE): What alternative wording would you propose, Councilor?

COUNCILOR TRAFFORD: "Dogs are not allowed in this Park without leads."

COUNCILOR HOGG: Mr. Chairman, I object. The order should be addressed to the owners, not to the dogs.

COUNCILOR TRAFFORD: That is a nice point. Very well then: "Owners of dogs are not allowed in the Park unless they keep them on leads."

COUNCILOR HOGG: Mr. Chairman, I object. Strictly speaking, this would prevent me as a dog-owner from leaving my dog in the back-garden at home and walking with Mrs. Hogg across the Park.

COUNCILOR TRAFFORD: Mr. Chairman, I suggest that our legalistic friend be asked to redraft the notice himself.

COUNCILOR HOGG: Mr. Chairman, since Councilor Trafford finds it so difficult to improve on my original wording, I accept. "Nobody without his dog on a lead is allowed in this Park."

COUNCILOR TRAFFORD: Mr. Chairman, I object. Strictly speaking, this notice would prevent me, as a citizen, who owns no dog, from walking in the Park without first acquiring one.

COUNCILOR HOGG (with some warmth): Very simply then: "Dogs must be led in this Park."

COUNCILOR TRAFFORD: Mr. Chairman, I object: This reads as if it were a general injunction to the Borough to lead their dogs into the Park.

Councilor Hogg interposed a remark for which he was called to order; upon his withdrawing it, it was directed to be expunged from the Minutes.

THE CHAIRMAN: Councilor Trafford, Councilor Hogg has had three tries, you have had only two. . . .

COUNCILOR TRAFFORD: "All dogs must be kept on leads in this Park."

THE CHAIRMAN: I see Councilor Hogg rising quite rightly to raise another objection. May I anticipate him with another amendment: "All dogs in this Park must be kept on the lead."

This draft was put to the vote and carried unanimously, with two abstentions.[2]

This little episode should make the worth of a precise language more obvious to dog lovers (or haters). The following exercise is designed to make this need more obvious to the businessman:

1. A machine with a cycle of 6 seconds is improved to the point where the machine is 80% faster. What is the cycle time of the new machine?

Answer: _____

A machine with a production rate of 600 pieces per hour is improved to the point where the machine is 80% faster. What is the production rate of the new machine?

Answer: _____

The two parts to the exercise above might well have reference to the same machine. (Certainly a 6-second cycle time is equivalent to an output rate of 600 units per hour.) It seems only reasonable, then, to suppose that the answers to the two problems should be consistent. Oddly enough the answers most people give are not consistent. But why should the same question be answered differ-

---

[2] Robert Graves and Alan Hodge, *The Reader Over Your Shoulder* (Macmillan Paperback Ed., 1961; New York: Macmillan Co., 1943), pp. 149–50.

ently depending on the way one chooses to express machine speed? On second thought, even if our answers are consistent, can we be certain that our interpretation is the same one the writer or speaker had in mind? Without stretching our imagination, it is possible to visualize a very costly misunderstanding stemming from what appears to be a simple and precise English phrase—"80 per cent faster."

Before going on, a word of warning is in order. Our over-all objective is to show how mathematics can be useful to the business manager. We cannot progress very far, however, without having the rules of algebra close at hand. The balance of this chapter, then, is a detour in the sense that the emphasis is on the rules rather than their use. We shall be reviewing the most important of the rules of algebra. As you progress, do not be discouraged if you find that once-learned rules have been quickly and completely forgotten. If this is the case, try to get help; come back to the difficult parts later if necessary; but at any rate, attempt to have the essential elements of this chapter fairly well under control before completing this text.

2. A Review of the Rules of Algebra

2.1 EXPONENTS, ROOTS, AND POWERS

Repeated multiplication by a factor in a product is indicated by a small number called an "exponent" placed above and to the right of the factor. Hence, the repeated multiplications indicated below may be written two ways:

As a product	*With an exponent*
$(a)(a)(a)$	a^3
$(ab)(ab)(ab)(ab)$	$(ab)^4$ or a^4b^4
$(x + 2y)(x + 2y)$	$(x + 2y)^2$

In the first case the exponent is three and the term is expressed "a to the third *power*" or "a cubed." In the second case the exponent is four and the term is expressed as "ab to the fourth" or "ab to the fourth power." In the last case the exponent is two and the term is expressed "the quantity x plus two y squared" or "the quantity $(x + 2y)$ to the second power."

The result of multiplying n factors each equal to x is called the *nth power of x* and is written x^n. If x is a *positive* number, then x^n will be *positive*. If x is a *negative* number then x^n will be *positive* if n is *even*, and *negative* if n is *odd*. Thus $2^3 = 2 \cdot 2 \cdot 2 = 8$, $(-2)^3 = (-2)(-2)(-2) = -8$, $2^4 = 16$, and $(-2)^4 = 16$.

The expression $\sqrt[n]{x}$ is referred to as *"the nth root of x."* If $n = 2$, so that the second or square root is indicated, it is customary to omit the 2 and write simply, $\sqrt{x}$. The nth root of x is the number which when raised to the nth power will equal x. If $y^n = x$, then $\sqrt[n]{x} = y$. Since $2^3 = 8$, then $\sqrt[3]{8} = 2$. It can be seen that the process of raising a number to a power and the process of extracting a root are related in much the same manner that multiplication and division are related:

$$\frac{a}{b} = c, a = bc; y^n = x, \sqrt[n]{x} = y.$$

Whenever an even root of a positive number is indicated, the root has more than one real value. For instance, $(+3)^4 = 81$, therefore, $\sqrt[4]{81} = +3$. However, $(-3)^4 = (-3)(-3)(-3)(-3) = 81$ also, therefore, $\sqrt[4]{81} = -3$ as well as $+3$. From this it can be seen that the fourth root of 81 has two real values, plus or minus 3 (usually written ± 3). Therefore, $\sqrt[4]{81} = \pm 3$.

Given an equation such as $a^2 = 9$, then $a = \pm \sqrt{9}$, or $a = \pm 3$. It is customary to let $\sqrt{9}$ represent the positive root and let $-\sqrt{9}$ represent the negative root. Therefore, $\sqrt{9}$ is understood to mean 3, not ± 3.

Since an odd power has the same sign as its root, it follows that an odd root has the same sign as its power. Consequently $\sqrt[3]{x}$ or $\sqrt[5]{x}$ must be positive when x is positive and negative when x is negative. For example, $\sqrt[3]{8} = 2$, $\sqrt[3]{-8} = -2$, $\sqrt[5]{-32} = -2$.

 2. Raise the following factors to the indicated power.

$5^2 \quad = \underline{\hspace{3cm}}$

$(-3)^4 = \underline{\hspace{3cm}}$

$(-6)^2 = \underline{\hspace{3cm}}$

$(-6)^3 = \underline{\hspace{3cm}}$

$(-5)^1 = \underline{\hspace{3cm}}$

$(2)^5 \quad = \underline{\hspace{3cm}}$

3. Find the values of x below.

$x^3 = 27$ $x = $ _____

$x^3 = -27$ $x = $ _____

$x^2 = 25$ $x = $ _____

$x^3 = 64$ $x = $ _____

$x^3 = -64$ $x = $ _____

$x^4 = 16$ $x = $ _____

2.2 LAWS OF EXPONENTS

Often one finds the same number involved as a factor several times, but raised to various powers. For this reason, rules for combining the various exponents of the same number are helpful in quickly reducing the complexity of the expression. For example, consider the following:

$$a \cdot a \cdot a \cdot a \cdot a = (a \cdot a) \cdot (a \cdot a \cdot a) = a^2 \cdot a^3 = a^5.$$

Clearly, the correct exponent for the last expression (5), is the total number of times a is a factor in the problem, regardless of where or how these factors are arranged. In general, then,

$$a^i \text{ times } a^j = a^{i \text{ plus } j}.$$

This is often reduced to the rather cryptic instruction "when you multiply, add exponents."

The adoption of this rule leads to several other rules automatically. For instance, consider the statement:

$$a^5 = a^4 a^1 = a^3 a^2 = a^5 a^0.$$

It seems perfectly in order according to our rule, except for the last exponent on the right side, the zero. What does a^0 mean? Take a as a factor no times at all? Mathematicians, choosing to be consistent, and noting that $x = x + 0$ by definition of the integer zero, have agreed that *anything*[3] to the zeroth power is *one*.

Having agreed upon this rule, it now becomes possible to consider the meaning of *negative* exponents. How could the expression a^{-3} be interpreted and still be consistent with all the rules above? Noting that $2 = 5 - 3$, and writing

---

[3] Except the number zero itself.

$$a^2 = a^5 a^{-3},$$

it must be that a^{-3} is whatever one must multiply a^5 by to get a^2. But to get a^2 from a^5 one must *divide* by a^3, because $a^2 a^3 = a^5$. Thus a^{-3} must be equal to $1/a^3$:

$$a^2 = a \cdot a = (\cancel{a} \cdot \cancel{a} \cdot \cancel{a} \cdot a \cdot a)\left(\frac{1}{\cancel{a} \cdot \cancel{a} \cdot \cancel{a}}\right)$$
$$= a^5 a^{-3}.$$

Having come this far, it is easy to verify that one subtracts exponents when dividing powers of a number:

$$a^8 \div a^3 = a^{8-3} = a^5.$$

Also, from the addition rule,

$$(a^2)^3 = (a^2)(a^2)(a^2) = (a \cdot a \cdot a \cdot a \cdot a \cdot a) = a^6 = a^{2 \text{ times } 3}.$$

When a power is raised to a power, then, one multiplies the exponents.

The rules for combining exponents can be summarized as follows:

$$(a^i)(a^j) = a^{i+j}$$
$$a^i \div a^j = a^{i-j}$$
$$a^0 = 1$$
$$a^{-i} = \frac{1}{a^i}$$
$$(a^i)^j = a^{ij}$$

4. Simplify the following expressions as much as possible:

$$a^5 a b a^{-6} b^2 = \underline{\hspace{4cm}}$$

$$x^{-5} b^2 b^3 x^6 b = \underline{\hspace{4cm}}$$

$$a^5 b^4 \div b^5 = \underline{\hspace{4cm}}$$

2.3 FRACTIONAL EXPONENTS

In section 2.1, the symbol $\sqrt[n]{x}$ was interpreted as "the nth root of x." This symbol is generally referred to as a *radical*. Any symbol, e.g., $\sqrt[3]{x}$ or $\sqrt[x]{3}$, is called a "radical."

Radicals, however, are awkward to write and usually not very convenient to use in computation. It would help if a better symbol were available. There is, in fact, and it is the result of mathematicians defining "the nth root of x to be equal to the $1/n$th power of *x*." That is $\sqrt[i]{x} = x^{1/i}$. In other words a radical can be written as a *fractional exponent.*

The advantages of the fractional exponents lie in the fact that they allow exponent division in a way that complements and is consistent with the laws of exponent addition, subtraction, and multiplication discussed in the previous paragraph. For example:

$$\sqrt[3]{8} = 8^{1/3} = 2$$
$$\sqrt[3]{2^3} = 2^{3/3} = 2$$
$$\sqrt[3]{32} = \sqrt[3]{2^5} = 2^{5/3}$$

The fact that radicals are the same as fractional exponents gives rise to the decimal exponents sometimes encountered. For instance, $\sqrt[4]{x} = x^{1/4} = x^{.25}$.

5. Find the integer value of:

$16^{3/4}$ _____ $27^{2/3}$ _____

6. Express the following using a fractional exponent:

$$\sqrt[b]{(x + y)^{-a}}$$ _____

7. Find the numerical value of:

$$(2^{.76})(2^{1.24})$$ _____

2.4 LOGARITHMS AS EXPONENTS

Most of the rules of exponents used in the previous exercises evolved early in the development of elementary algebra, primarily as a convenient shorthand for recording the result of repeated multiplications or divisions. It was not until the seventeenth century that the theory of *logarithms* was invented, which is now generally considered to be one of the major achievements of that century in mathematics. Logarithms simplified computations to such an extent that it is difficult to estimate the time they saved astronomers and others through the years who have been faced with tedious calculations. Although the digital computer has practically replaced logarithms for large-scale computational efforts, they are still useful for on-the-spot numerical calculations. For this reason, the last section of this chapter covers the computational uses of the theory of logarithms.

In this section we shall be concerned only with the *concept* of a logarithm; for this alone, quite apart from the computational uses of logarithms, is very helpful in simplifying and manipulating certain kinds of mathematical problems. One example of this use will come up in Chapter 5, when we study the exponential trend, a very useful kind of relationship between two variables. So, let us begin by carefully defining what a logarithm *is:*

A LOGARITHM IS AN EXPONENT

This definition might seem a bit too simple, especially since it says little more than the title of this section. And yet that is all there is to know; once you have learned how to handle exponents, you can handle logarithms. The only difference is in the *notation.*

As it turns out, for most people this simply is not a good enough explanation. That is why the following definition should be *memorized:*

> If b is any positive number (other than the number 1) and $b^y = x$, then the exponent y is called the *logarithm of x to the base b*. In symbols: if $b^y = x$, then $y = \log_b x$.

Using this definition, $2^3 = 8$, therefore $\log_2 8 = 3$. Also $\log_3 9 = 2$ because $3^2 = 9$, and $\log_9 3 = 1/2$ because $(9)^{1/2} = 3$.

It is easy to confuse the roles played by the three numbers b, y, and x unless the definition is learned carefully. Notice that a logarithm is an exponent, as we said; that is, $y = \log_b x$ means that y is the exponent to which we must raise the *base b* in order get the *number x*. We can express a particular problem several different ways, as follows:

- What is the logarithm of 243 to the base 3?
- $\log_3 243 = ?$
- To what power must the number 3 be raised to yield 243?
- $3^x = 243; x = ?$

The answer in all cases is 5, because 5 is the logarithm of 243 to the base 3.

 8. Test your knowledge of the definition of a logarithm on the following examples, the first of which has been worked for you:

$$\log_5 x = 2; = \quad \underline{\quad 25 \quad}$$

$$\log_7 49 = y \; ; \qquad\qquad y = \underline{\hspace{2cm}}$$

$$\log_{10} 10 = y \; ; \qquad\qquad y = \underline{\hspace{2cm}}$$

$$\log_b 144 = 2 \; ; \qquad\qquad b = \underline{\hspace{2cm}}$$

$$\log_b 4 = 0.5 \; ; \qquad\qquad b = \underline{\hspace{2cm}}$$

$$\log_8 x = 3 \; ; \qquad\qquad x = \underline{\hspace{2cm}}$$

$$\log_5 x = -2 \; ; \qquad\qquad x = \underline{\hspace{2cm}}$$

$$\log_b x = 0 \; ; \qquad\qquad x = \underline{\hspace{2cm}}$$

As you observed in the above exercises, logarithms (being exponents) can be fractional or negative. For example, $\log_{32} 2 = 1/5$ because $32^{1/5} = \sqrt[5]{32} = 2$. Also, $\log_{10} 0.001 = -3$ because $10^{-3} = 0.001$. Also, $\log_4 8 = 3/2$ because $(4)^{3/2} = \sqrt[2]{4^3} = 8$.

Consider the equation $y = \log_b (b^A)$. What is the value of y? By definition, y is the power to which the base b must be raised to get the number b^A. But that power is just A. In other words $\log_b(b^A) = A$, so $y = A$ no matter what b is. By using this same idea, we are able to solve equations containing a variable in an exponent. For example, we solve the equation:

$$2^x = N,$$

for x by "taking the log of both sides" as follows:

$$\log_2 (2^x) = \log_2 N$$
$$x = \log_2 N.$$

Before leaving logarithms temporarily, let us consider one further point. In discussing exponents we stated the rules by which exponents can be combined. The first of these rules was:

$$(a^i)(a^j) = a^{i+j}.$$

Suppose we let $M = a^i$ and $N = a^j$, in which case $MN = a^{i+j}$. Taking logarithms to the base a in these last three equations gives:

$$\log_a M \;\;\; = \log_a(a^i) \;\;\; = i$$
$$\log_a N \;\;\; = \log_a(a^j) \;\;\; = j$$
$$\log_a (MN) = \log_a(a^{i+j}) = i + j.$$

since $(i) + (j) = (i + j)$, it follows that:

$$\log_a (MN) = \log_a M + \log_a N.$$

This rule says "when you multiply, add logarithms," which corresponds exactly to the rule which says "when you multiply, add exponents."

The exponential trend equation is usually written $y = ae^{bx}$. We will learn more about this equation in Chapter 5, but for the moment let us rewrite it using logarithms:

$$y = (a)(e^{bx})$$
$$\log_e y = \log_e a + \log_e(e^{bx})$$
$$\log_e y = \log_e a + bx.$$

The first step is correct by the rule on adding logarithms, and the last step follows from the definition of a logarithm. Although this may look more complicated than the equation we started with, for some purposes it is better, as we shall see. Meanwhile, try your hand at some exercises (two of which are already worked out for you):

9. $y = a^2$ $\log_a y =$ _____ 2 _____

   $y = a^2 b$ $\log_a y =$ ____ $2 + \log_a b$ ____

   $y = a^2 b$ $\log_b y =$ _____

   $y = ab^x$ $\log_b y =$ _____

   $y = ax^b$ $\log_2 y =$ _____

2.5 POLYNOMIALS

The algebraic *expression* $6x - 5x^2 y + 10y - \sqrt{2}$ consists of the four terms: $(6x)$, $(-5x^2 y)$, $(+10y)$, and $(-\sqrt{2})$. Algebraic expressions such as $3(x - y + 2) + 2(y - 3)$ can be simplified to $3x - 3y + 6 + 2y - 6 = 3x - y$. This simplified expression has only two terms and is called a *binomial*. In general, an expression is named by the number of terms it has when written in its simplest form. A *monomial* has one term, a *binomial* two, etc. The categorical name for expressions having more than one term is *polynomial*. Note also that we define as *terms* the parts of an algebraic expression that are connected simply by the operation of addition or subtraction.

Examples:

$- 9xy^2 z$ is a *monomial* because it is an expres-
$\overline{5w}$ sion in which there are no terms con-
          nected by addition or subtraction.

$5x^2 - 3x - y^2$ is a *polynomial*.

$(2x - y) - 2x$ is a *monomial* because in its simplest form it reduces to the single term, $-y$.

2.6   OPERATIONS WITH MONOMIALS

The multiplication or division of a monomial by a monomial is relatively simple. Multiplication, of course, may be indicated by parentheses as in $(3a^2b)(-2ab)$ or by the absence of a special symbol as in xy. Usually the parentheses are removed after indicated multiplications have been carried out to the fullest extent possible. Division is indicated by the fractional form a/b. Care must be taken in regard to signs and the rules governing exponents. For instance,

$$(3a^2b)(-2ab) = -6a^3b^2$$
$$\frac{144xy^2z^3}{24xyz} = \frac{144\cancel{x}\cancel{y}y\cancel{z}zz}{24\cancel{x}\cancel{y}\cancel{z}} = 6yz^2.$$

10. Perform the indicated operations.

$(14ab)(2ab^2c) =$ _____

$\dfrac{-6a^3b^2}{3a^2b} =$ _____

$(-10x)(-5xy)(-xyz) =$ _____

$\dfrac{(-7ab)(-5a^2c)}{-35bc} =$ _____

2.7   OPERATIONS WITH POLYNOMIALS

To multiply a polynomial by a monomial—for example, to multiply $(5x + 2y - 4)$ by $3x$—*every term* of the polynomial must be multiplied by the monomial. To illustrate:

$$(3x)(5x + 2y - 4) = 15x^2 + 6xy - 12x.$$

If, instead of $3x$, the monomial had been $-3x$, the result would be

$$(-3x)(5x + 2y - 4) = -15x^2 - 6xy + 12x.$$

The effect of the negative sign is to *change the sign of every term* in the answer. In an expression such as $x - (3x + y)$, the minus sign in front of the parentheses is equivalent to multiplying the expression within the parentheses by -1. This, likewise, has the effect of changing the signs of all terms within the parentheses.

$$x - (3x + y) = x - 3x - y = -2x - y.$$

To divide a polynomial by a monomial, the process is similar, i.e., each term is divided separately by the monomial and all signs in the result are changed if the monomial is negative. To illustrate:

$$\frac{(-2a^2b + 6a^3 - 2a^2)}{-2a^2} = b - 3a + 1.$$

11. Perform the indicated multiplications and simplify where possible.
$$-2a(-3x) + 2x(x - 3a) = \underline{\hspace{2cm}}.$$

12. Perform the indicated operations:
$$\frac{-x(x^2y - y^3)}{-xy} = \underline{\hspace{2cm}}.$$

13. Between each pair of the expressions below put $=$ or $\neq$ whichever is appropriate.

$$\left[\frac{a-b}{a-c}\right]\left(\frac{3x}{4y}\right) \qquad \frac{3}{4}\left[\frac{x(b-a)}{y(c-a)}\right]$$

$$a(b - ac + x) \qquad a[(b - ac) + x]$$

$$\frac{2x - y}{3} \qquad \frac{y - 2x}{3}$$

$$-\frac{1}{2}(a - b) \qquad \frac{b - a}{2}$$

$$a(b - c + d) \qquad ab - c + d$$

3.   Mathematical Relationships

3.1 EQUATIONS

One of the most familiar of all mathematical symbols is the equal sign ($=$). Unfortunately, it is used to denote a variety of relationships, all of which concern equality but which differ sufficiently to confuse the careless reader of a mathematical text. For example, if you write "$\sqrt{9} = 3$" it means that the symbols on both sides of the $=$ mark are symbols for the same thing, in this case the number "three." In geometry, the statement "angle ABC = angle ACB" means that the angle with B as a vertex is equal to the angle whose vertex is C, i.e., they are equal in the sense that one can be exactly superimposed upon the other. In FORTRAN computer programing, if you write the statement "LOT = 2*MUCH" it is a computer instruction to retrieve the fixed point number stored in location

MUCH, multiply it by the number 2, and store the resulting fixed point product in location LOT. As always, the mathematician's symbols mean just what he says they do, nothing else.

In algebra, and in fact the great bulk of mathematics, a sentence like "$R = S$" has a more narrow meaning. Such a statement is called an *equation,* and the R and S are referred to as the *sides* of the equation. To make any sense, R and S must each be algebraic expressions, i.e., a constant, variable, or formula. An equation, therefore, corresponds to the very simplest type of English sentence: (a noun) is (a noun). If both sides are constants (proper nouns in English) the equation is simply stating an equivalence between two names for the same thing, such as "$\$1 = 100\cancel{c}$" or "Indiana = The Hoosier State" or "$7 =$ VII."

Some people might wonder why it is necessary to allow for the possibility of having two names for the same thing in the language of mathematics which is supposedly so concise. In solving a problem, it ought to be a simple matter to assign a single name to each quantity which appeared. The fact is, however, that much of the power of mathematics arises from *not* doing this. Instead, the usual procedure is to go ahead and introduce an arbitrary name for a quantity—since one is unable to determine whether he has previously named it or not—and then move on to the eventual discovery that it *was* previously named and, what is more important, to determine what that previously assigned name was. Most of the "word problems" of high school algebra are based on this simple idea, as the following example will illustrate:

"John is nine years older than he was when he was one half as old as he will be a year from now. How old is he?" To solve such an elementary problem, one chooses a name for John's age now — the determination of which constitutes the problem's solution. Having selected, say, the symbol "x" as the name for John's age, the student then restates the problem using this name, and after suitable manipulation, arrives at the final step. If done correctly, this will be the short sentence "$x = 19$," which states the synonymity of two terms (the symbol x and the numeral 19). Thus, the student discovers that a perfectly good name for John's age already existed—the numeral 19—and that the invented name was no longer necessary!

The important point here is that the symbol "19" has a widely understood meaning, so that announcing it as the solution has the advantage of being highly communicative. After restating the question "How old is John?" as "What is the value of x?" the solution proceeds as follows:

$$x = \text{nine years more than one half of one}$$
more than x
$$x = 9 + (\tfrac{1}{2})(x + 1)$$
$$x = 9 + \tfrac{1}{2}x + \tfrac{1}{2}$$

or (finally)

$$x = 19.$$

While all answers are technically correct, only the last one is any good for communicating to others, because all the rest involve (in the right-hand term) the symbol "x" which does *not* mean the same thing to *everybody*—in fact, it was defined for the special purposes of this problem only, and in a few minutes it may be used to stand for something else entirely. It is *treated* as a variable temporarily only because we had not yet concluded which among many possible numerical candidates should be uniquely elected to stand for John's age, in the light of the information at hand about John. After the election of the "19," there is left a superfluous name ("x") for the number 19, which can now be discarded.

Because this procedure of assigning temporary names to unknown objects and then writing (algebraic) statements about these objects is so common in mathematics, a great many equations containing variables face the mathematical modeler. Such an equation is $A^2 + A = 6$, where A is a variable. Technically speaking, this is a *conditional equation,* because it is a true statement only for a restricted number of values for the variable A. ($A = 2$ is one of two such values.)

Some equations are true no matter what values are substituted for the variables, such as the statement $x(x + 2) = x^2 + 2x$. As you can verify, this statement is true for any number that you care to substitute for the variable x. Such equations are called *identities.* Often, identities are distinguished by the special mark ($\equiv$) instead of an equal sign. Because the most interesting kind of equation is the conditional one, which usually needs to be *solved* for the values of the variable which *satisfy* the equation, the word "conditional" is usually understood, referring simply to an equation to be solved.

3.2 ALGEBRAIC OPERATIONS
INVOLVING ZERO

Zero is represented by a particular point on the line representing all integers. It must, therefore, be properly considered a member of the number system and not simply something to be identified with "nothing." Nevertheless, it is a special kind of number to which the following special rules apply.

1. The *sum* of any number and zero is the number itself: $x + 0 = x$.
2. The *difference* between any number and zero is the number itself: $x - 0 = x$.
3. The *product* of any number and zero is zero: $(x)(0) = 0$.
4. Zero divided by any number is zero: $0/x = 0$.
5. *BUT* division of any number by zero is *inadmissible*: i.e., $x/0$ is not allowed in ordinary algebra.

The reason why division by zero is not allowed can best be illustrated by an example. Consider the following proof (ugh!) that $3 = 0$. If we let $x = 3$, then $x^2 = 3x$ and $x^2 - 9 = 3x - 9$.

1. $x^2 - 9 = 3x - 9$
2. $(x - 3)(x + 3) = 3(x - 3)$
3. $\dfrac{(x-3)(x + 3)}{(x-3)} = \dfrac{3(x-3)}{(x-3)}$
4. $x + 3 = 3$
5. $x = 0$
6. but $x = 3$
7. therefore $3 = 0$

Although this spurious proof may appear plausible, a fatal mistake occurred in dividing line 2 by $(x - 3)$ to get line 4, as shown in line 3. This is inadmissable since $(x-3) = 0$ when $x = 3$. In certain situations it may be necessary to specify that one of the variables not equal a certain number in order to avoid division by zero. For instance, one could write the equation:

$$\frac{x^2 - 9}{x - 3} = x + 3$$

provided it was specified that $x \neq 3$, since if x did equal 3, $x - 3$ would equal zero, creating the inadmissible operation of division by zero.

In the case of the product of two numbers equaling zero, say $xy = 0$, either x or y or both must equal zero. For example, the equation $A^2 + A = 6$ can be rewritten as $(A + 3)(A - 2) = 0$. Now if $A = -3$, then $(-3 + 3)(-3 - 2) = (0)(-5) = 0$ or if $A = +2$, then $(2 + 3)(2 - 2) = (5)(0) = 0$. Therefore, either $A = -3$ or $A = 2$ satisfies the equation, and the resulting values are called *solutions* to the equation.

14. Indicate after each statement whether you consider it to be correct or incorrect by circling C or I.

$$\frac{9a - 8a - a}{3a} = 0$$ C or I

$$\frac{12b - 9b}{9b - 9b} = \frac{4}{3}$$ C or I

If $5(x - 7) = 0$, then $x = 7$ C or I

3.3 SOLVING EQUATIONS

Solving equations was the core of every algebra course and often the whole objective of the course. The equations, you recall, came in many shapes and sizes all of which had fancy names. Sometimes they had one "unknown" and the object of finding a solution was to discover the numerical value which, when substituted for the variable, would satisfy the conditions of the equation. For example, to solve the equation $3x + 17 = 15 + x$ for x one might proceed as follows:

$$3x + 17 = 15 + x$$
$$3x - x = 15 - 17$$
$$2x = -2$$
$$x = -1.$$

This could then be checked by substituting $x = -1$ in the original equation.

$$3(-1) + 17 = 15 + (-1)$$
$$14 = 14.$$

The result of this substitution indicates that the solution is correct since the equality is verified, i.e., $14 = 14$.

Sometimes the equations had many unknowns (variables) and a solution in terms of one of them was required. Such solutions were called "general" solutions as opposed to "numerical" solutions. For example, to solve $3y + w - x = 27y$ for x, the object was to perform the manipulations required to get x all by itself on the left-hand side of the equality.

$$3y + w - x = 27y$$
$$-x = 27y - 3y - w$$
$$x = w - 24y.$$

Solving the same equation for y:

$$x = w - 24y$$
$$24y = w - x$$
$$y = \frac{w - x}{24}.$$

Often there was more than one unknown to be solved for. This required at least as many equations (called "simultaneous equations") as there were variables. One of two methods was used in this case. One involved eliminating one of the variables by subtracting one equation from the other, as illustrated below:

$$4x + y = 10 \qquad \text{two equations to be solved}$$
$$3x + 2y = 5 \qquad \text{simultaneously}$$

$$8x + 2y = 20 \qquad \text{(first equation times 2)}$$
$$\underline{3x + 2y = 5}$$
$$5x = 15 \qquad \text{(the result of subtraction)}$$

or $\qquad\qquad x = 3$

$$4(3) + y = 10 \qquad \text{(putting } x = 3 \text{ in first equation)}$$
$$12 + y = 10$$

and $\qquad\qquad y = -2.$

Hence, $(x = 3, y = -2)$ is the desired solution.

The second method, called the "method of substitution," involved substituting the general solution for one variable in one equation into the second equation.

$$4x + y = 10$$
$$3x + 2y = 5$$

from the first equation

$$y = 10 - 4x$$

substituting this value for y in the second equation:

$$3x + 2(10 - 4x) = 5$$
$$3x + 20 - 8x = 5$$
$$-5x = -15$$
$$x = 3$$

but $\qquad\qquad y = 10 - 4x$
$$ = 10 - 4(3)$$

or $\qquad\qquad y = -2.$

In both methods, of course, the same solution results, i.e., $x = 3$, $y = -2$. By substituting these values into the original two equations, both are satisfied, of course.

In general, the fundamental manipulative rules of algebra are based on the principle that the integrity of the equality must be retained in the process of solving an equation. Some of these rules are as follows:

In any equation the equality is not destroyed by:

1. Adding the same quantity to both sides of the equation.
2. Subtracting the same quantity from both sides.
3. Multiplying each side by the same quantity.
4. Dividing each side by the same quantity (except zero.)
5. Raising each side to the same power or extracting the same root.
6. Taking logarithms of each side (as illustrated in Section 2.4).
7. Any term may be transposed from one side to another provided its sign is changed.

These rules may be applied in any order; however, it is usually useful to clear the equation of radicals and fractions as early as possible. In the balance of this paragraph we will review the application of these rules to the most important type of equations, that is equations of the first degree (involving variables raised to the power 1).

Example:

$$\text{Solve } \frac{3x}{2} - \frac{\Sigma xy}{3} + x = 3 \text{ for } \Sigma xy.$$

(Note: Σxy is treated as a single variable.)

1. Multiply both sides by 6:
$$9x - 2\Sigma xy + 6x = 18.$$
2. Subtract $15x$ from both sides:
$$-2\Sigma xy = 18 - 15x.$$
3. Divide both sides by -2:
$$\Sigma xy = \frac{15}{2}x - 9.$$

4. To check the solution substitute $(\frac{15}{2}x - 9)$ in place of Σxy in the original equation:

$$\frac{3x}{2} - \frac{1}{3}\left(\frac{15}{2}x - 9\right) + x = 3$$

$$\frac{3x}{2} - \frac{5x}{2} + 3 + x = 3$$

$$-\frac{2x}{2} + \frac{2x}{2} = 3 - 3$$

$$0 = 0.$$

15. Solve the following equations:

$$\frac{2\sqrt{N}}{6} = 5 \qquad\qquad N = \underline{\hspace{2cm}}$$

$$a = \frac{(b-1)}{b} \qquad\qquad b = \underline{\hspace{2cm}}$$

Example:

Solve for a and b in the following simultaneous equations:

(1) $\Sigma y = Na + b\Sigma x$

(2) $\Sigma xy = a\Sigma x + b\Sigma x^2.$

1. From equation (1):

$$a = \frac{\Sigma y - b\Sigma x}{N} = \frac{\Sigma y}{N} - \frac{b\Sigma x}{N}.$$

2. Substituting this value for a in equation (2) and solving for b:

$$\Sigma xy = \Sigma x\left(\frac{\Sigma y - b\Sigma x}{N}\right) + b\Sigma x^2$$

$$N\Sigma xy = \Sigma x\Sigma y - b(\Sigma x)^2 + Nb\Sigma x^2$$

$$N\Sigma xy - \Sigma x\Sigma y = b[N\Sigma x^2 - (\Sigma x)^2]$$

$$b = \frac{N\Sigma xy - \Sigma x\Sigma y}{N\Sigma x^2 - (\Sigma x)^2}.$$

The particular equations solved above are called "normal equations." We will return to this solution of the normal equations again in Chapter 5.

16.   Solve for x, y and z:

(1) $x + y + z = 12$

(2) $2x \qquad + z = 10$

(3) $x - y + z = 2$

$$x = \underline{\hspace{3cm}}$$

$$y = \underline{\hspace{3cm}}$$

$$z = \underline{\hspace{3cm}}$$

3.4 INEQUATIONS

The algebra of *inequations* or *inequalities*, with which many of you may not be familiar, is included here because of its particular importance in business problems. It is important for it provides the means of expressing mathematically the explicit constraints that influence decisions and restrict freedom of choice. For example, plant capacity may permit the production of 10,000 units per year, but any number of units may actually be produced provided this capacity is not exceeded. There may be a certain maximum number of hours of computer time available, but they may or may not all be utilized. Decisions regarding investment in plant and equipment may be governed by a policy or even just the desire of not falling beneath a certain minimum ratio of return on investment. A warehouse may be restricted in capacity, but it need not always be filled to that capacity. And there are many more such examples.

Unlike most familiar mathematics, it is common to find that there are many possible or feasible solutions to problems involving inequalities (inequations). Because of this, special mathematical techniques (e.g., mathematical programing) are required to determine which of the many feasible solutions is optimum. We will consider this matter later (in the next text) under the heading of linear programing. For the moment, however, we will limit our discussion to the basic algebraic operations involving inequalities.

If "a is greater than b," ($a > b$), then $a - b$ must be positive. If "a is less than b," ($a < b$), then $a - b$ is negative. From these properties, we can see that an inequality remains an inequality of the same order, i.e., in the same direction, if the same number is added to (or subtracted from) both sides of the inequality.

Example:

$$\text{If } a < b \text{ then}$$
$$a + 5 < b + 5 \text{ and}$$
$$a - 12 < b - 12.$$

This can be seen more clearly by substituting numerical values in place of a and b.

$$\text{If } a = 5 \text{ and } b = 7 \text{ then}$$
$$5 < 7$$
$$5 + 5 < 7 + 5 \text{ or } 10 < 12$$
$$5 - 12 < 7 - 12 \text{ or } -7 < -5.$$

Like equations, both sides of inequations can be multiplied by the same constant. One must be careful, however, because it makes a difference whether the constant is "greater than" or "less than" zero. When the constant is greater than zero ($k > 0$), the order of the inequality is *not* changed. When the constant is less than zero ($k < 0$), the *order* of the inequality *is changed*. This can be illustrated as follows:

When $k > 0$, or positive:

> If $a > b$, then $ka > kb$
> Substituting numerical values: $a = 5, b = 2, k = 7$
> $5 > 2$ and
> $(7)(5) > (7)(2)$ or $35 > 14$

When $k < 0$, or negative:

> If $a > b$, then $ka < kb$
> (note the change in the order of the inequality)
> Substituting numerical values; $a = 5, b = 2, k = -7$
> $5 > 2$ and
> $(-7)(5) < (-7)(2)$ or $-35 < -14$.

An inequality that is true for all values of the variables is called an *unconditional inequality*. For example, $4x + 3 < 4x + 7$ is an unconditional equality. Inequalities that hold only for certain values of the variables are called *conditional inequalities*. The inequality, $3x - 4 < 2$, for example, is true only under the condition that $x < 2$. This can be shown as follows:

$$3x - 4 < 2$$
$$3x < 6$$
$$x < 2.$$

Simple inequations can be solved by the same methods that apply to equations. The only additional point to watch for is the reversal of the direction of the inequality caused by multiplication by a negative number. (Changing of signs on either side, of course, is equivalent to multiplying by -1.)

Example:
$$\text{Solve } 2x + 7 < 4.$$

1. Add -7 to both sides:
$$2x < -3.$$

2. Multiply by ½:
$$x < -\frac{3}{2}.$$

Example:

What value of x satisfies the inequation $4x - 3 \leq 7$

1. Add 3 to each member:

$$4x \leq 10$$

2. Multiply by ¼:

$$x \leq \frac{5}{2}$$

17. For what values of x is $2x - 3 > 1$?

Answer: _____

18. For what values of x is $4 - 3x > 10$?

Answer: _____

19. Try to show that if a and b are any two integers, that the following inequality is always true:

$$ab \leq \frac{a^2 + b^2}{2}$$

3.5 GRAPHIC RELATIONSHIPS

Let us dodge the issue of trying to define "relationship" and go about the business of demonstrating a number of different ways in which mathematical relationships may be expressed. After doing this you will probably recognize that the notion of relationship between quantitative variables is already a familiar one.

To illustrate a *first* way of describing a mathematical relationship, consider the following: "The deal is this: for each fleet car you rent, we charge you a flat rate of $660 a year. On top of that there is a nominal surcharge of 2 1/2 cents a mile, up to 20,000 miles, that is. Anything over 20,000 miles is free; in other words, you stop paying the mileage charge after that." This is a *verbal* expression of the relationship between the variable *mileage* and the variable *cost*. Since cost and mileage are measured numerically, they are called quantitative variables. For some purposes, verbalizing is an excellent way of expressing and communicating such relationships.

A *second* way to describe the same relationship is by a *table* showing some corresponding values of the two variables. Such a table might look like this:

Mileage	5,000	10,000	15,000	20,000	25,000
Cost	$ 785	910	1,035	1,160	1,160

This contains a selection of corresponding values of the variables, but theoretically it could be expanded to whatever size might be required. This too is a perfectly good expression of the relationship between cost and mileage.

A *third* way of expressing the same relationship is by an algebraic *equation*. If we let *"c"* represent cost and *"m"* mileage, the relationship would look like this:

$$c = 660 + .025m \qquad \text{if } m \leq 20{,}000,$$
$$c = 1{,}160 \qquad\qquad \text{if } m > 20{,}000.$$

This expression is more general than the table and more useful, too, except when you happen to be interested in the cost at exactly 10,000 miles, or 15,000, etc. It is certainly more economical to write the expression this way than in words. But the most important advantage in expressing the relationship like this, i.e., using mathematical symbols, is that it opens the door to the use of mathematics.

Still a *fourth* way of expressing this relationship is through use of a *graph*. At this point, however, let us leave the "fleet car" example (to which we will return) just long enough to mention very briefly the relationship between algebraic and graphic expressions of straight lines. This is a topic from analytic geometry which we will see more of in Chapters 5 and 6.

Suppose you sell bananas on a straight commission basis. Your commission is 10 cents a bunch. If x is the number of bunches you sell and y is your commission in dollars, then the relationship is $y = .10x$ and the graph of this looks like:

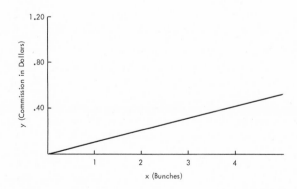

If your commission were raised to 20 cents or 30 cents or 40 cents a bunch, the graphs would look like this:

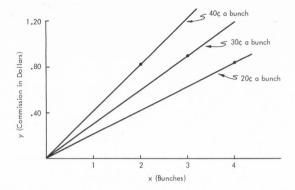

Notice that as the commission goes up, the slope of the graph gets steeper. The slope is defined as the number of units change on the y-axis for each single unit of change on the x-axis. More crudely, "the slope is however much the line goes up for each unit it goes across." Looking at the graph of the equation $y = .10x$, we can see that for each unit on the x-axis (for each bunch of bananas) the line goes up .10 units on the y-axis (or $.10). The slope of this line, therefore, is .10 which is the same .10 that appeared in the initial equation.

If we were to write equations for the other graphs illustrated, we would have $y = .20x$, $y = .30x$ etc., and the corresponding slopes would be found to be .20, .30, . . . respectively. Given this information we can now write a more general equation, $y = bx$, for the "family" of graphs similar to those illustrated in which b is a constant representing the slope of the line.

Now let us change the pay system slightly. Under the new system you still get the 10 cents commission, but in addition, you get a hazardous duty bonus of 50 cents. (This is intended to compensate you for the risk of being bitten by a tarantula while handling the bananas.)

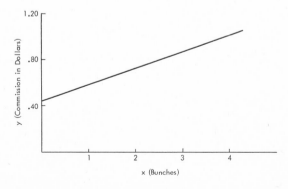

Under this new pay scheme, you can count on earning 50 cents even before you sell your first bunch of bananas. In other words, if $x = 0$,

y will still equal 50 cents, so the equation now becomes:
$$y = .50 + .10x.$$
From this we can see that the graph starts at a point where $x = 0$ and $y = .50$. The slope does not change; it is still .10.

In general, then, the equation of a straight line may be written as:
$$y = a + bx,$$
where a and b are constants; "b" is the *slope* of the line and "a" is the point where the graph crosses the y scale at $x = 0$. "a" is called the *y-intercept*.

Now if $a = 0$ (that is, if it is just dropped from the equation) the graph starts at $x = 0$, $y = 0$ (called the "origin"). If $b = 0$ (that is, if the term bx is dropped from the equation) the graph is just a horizontal straight line at $y = a$.

With this background now, let us return to the "fleet car" example and graph the relationship between cost and mileage expressed by the equations.

$$c = 660 + .025m \qquad \text{if } m \leq 20,000$$
$$c = 1,160 \qquad\qquad \text{if } m > 20,000.$$

The graph looks like this:

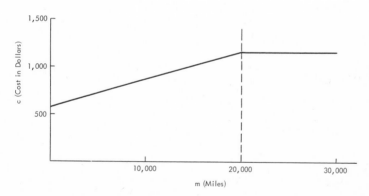

With a little knowledge of analytic geometry, it would have been easy to draw this graph by recognizing both algebraic equations as straight lines. For example, the equation $c = 660 + .025m$ is in the same form as $y = a + bx$, therefore, the y-intercept occurs at $c = 660$ and from this point it rises .025 dollars on the c scale for each mile on the m scale (a slope of .025). It stops at $m = 20,000$, since this equation applies only when $m \leq 20,000$. The equation $c = 1,160$ is the same form as $y = a$, therefore, it is a horizontal line at the value $c = 1,160$ for any value of $m > 20,000$.

The *graph*, like the other three methods of expressing quantitative relationships, has its own unique advantages and disadvantages. For instance, it shows directly *all* the corresponding values of the variables over the range of interest, not just the selected set of values displayed by the table. The disadvantage of the graph is that it cannot be manipulated from a mathematical point of view as can algebraic equations.

To summarize, we have demonstrated four ways of expressing relationships between quantitative variables: (1) verbally, (2) by table, (3) algebraic equation, and (4) graphs. Each is important and has its own advantages.

If our interest in expressing such a relationship in the first place is to perform a subsequent mathematical analysis, then the latter two methods are by far the most valuable. The ability to recognize and express such relationships is an important first step in using mathematics. For if one intends to operate in the language of mathematics, it is essential that the ingredients of the problem be translated into that language. The following exercises are intended to illustrate this translation back and forth.

20. In the box provided, sketch the graph of the following equation:

$$y = -20x + 500 \text{ when } 5 \leq x \leq 20.$$

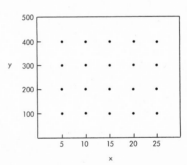

21. Using this graph complete the following table.

x	. . . .	5	10	15	20
y	. . . .	—	—	—	—

22. "Our experience has been that there is a linear relationship between volume and selling price, at least between the range of $5 and $20 per unit. At $5 a unit we can sell 400 units, but raising the price to $20 results in sales of only 100 units."

Is this statement the same relationship as in 20 and 21 above?

Circle One

Yes   No

23. If you circled "yes," label the variables x and y.

x represents   _____

y "   _____

Common Logarithms

N	0	1	2	3	4	5	6	7	8	9
10	0000	0043	0086	0128	0170	0212	0253	0294	0334	0374
11	0414	0453	0492	0531	0569	0607	0645	0682	0719	0755
12	0792	0828	0864	0899	0934	0969	1004	1038	1072	1106
13	1139	1173	1206	1239	1271	1303	1335	1367	1399	1430
14	1461	1492	1523	1553	1584	1614	1644	1673	1703	1732
15	1761	1790	1818	1847	1875	1903	1931	1959	1987	2014
16	2041	2068	2095	2122	2148	2175	2201	2227	2253	2279
17	2304	2330	2355	2380	2405	2430	2455	2480	2504	2529
18	2553	2577	2601	2625	2648	2672	2695	2718	2742	2765
19	2788	2810	2833	2856	2878	2900	2923	2945	2967	2989
20	3010	3032	3054	3075	3096	3118	3139	3160	3181	3201
21	3222	3243	3263	3284	3304	3324	3345	3365	3385	3404
22	3424	3444	3464	3483	3502	3522	3541	3560	3579	3598
23	3617	3636	3655	3674	3692	3711	3729	3747	3766	3784
24	3802	3820	3838	3856	3874	3892	3909	3927	3945	3962
25	3979	3997	4014	4031	4048	4065	4082	4099	4116	4133
26	4150	4166	4183	4200	4216	4232	4249	4265	4281	4298
27	4314	4330	4346	4362	4378	4393	4409	4425	4440	4456
28	4472	4487	4502	4518	4533	4548	4564	4579	4594	4609
29	4624	4639	4654	4669	4683	4698	4713	4728	4742	4757
30	4771	4786	4800	4814	4829	4843	4857	4871	4886	4900
31	4914	4928	4942	4955	4969	4983	4997	5011	5024	5038
32	5051	5065	5079	5092	5105	5119	5132	5145	5159	5172
33	5185	5198	5211	5224	5237	5250	5263	5276	5289	5302
34	5315	5328	5340	5353	5366	5378	5391	5403	5416	5428
35	5441	5453	5465	5478	5490	5502	5514	5527	5539	5551
36	5563	5575	5587	5599	5611	5623	5635	5647	5658	5670
37	5682	5694	5705	5717	5729	5740	5752	5763	5775	5786
38	5798	5809	5821	5832	5843	5855	5866	5877	5888	5899
39	5911	5922	5933	5944	5955	5966	5977	5988	5999	6010
40	6021	6031	6042	6053	6064	6075	6085	6096	6107	6117
41	6128	6138	6149	6160	6170	6180	6191	6201	6212	6222
42	6232	6243	6253	6263	6274	6284	6294	6304	6314	6325
43	6336	6345	6355	6365	6375	6385	6395	6405	6415	6425
44	6435	6444	6454	6464	6474	6484	6493	6503	6513	6522
45	6532	6542	6551	6561	6571	6580	6590	6599	6609	6618
46	6628	6637	6646	6656	6665	6675	6684	6693	6702	6712
47	6721	6730	6739	6749	6758	6767	6776	6785	6794	6803
48	6812	6821	6830	6839	6848	6857	6866	6875	6884	6893
49	6902	6911	6920	6928	6937	6946	6955	6964	6972	6981
50	6990	6998	7007	7016	7024	7033	7042	7050	7059	7067
51	7076	7084	7093	7101	7110	7118	7126	7135	7143	7152
52	7160	7168	7177	7185	7193	7202	7210	7218	7226	7235
53	7243	7251	7259	7267	7275	7284	7292	7300	7308	7316
54	7324	7332	7340	7348	7356	7364	7372	7380	7388	7396

Common Logarithms (Continued)

N	0	1	2	3	4	5	6	7	8	9
55	7404	7412	7419	7427	7435	7443	7451	7459	7466	7474
56	7482	7490	7497	7505	7513	7520	7528	7536	7543	7551
57	7559	7566	7574	7582	7589	7597	7604	7612	7619	7627
58	7634	7642	7649	7657	7664	7672	7679	7686	7694	7701
59	7709	7716	7723	7731	7738	7745	7752	7760	7767	7774
60	7782	7789	7796	7803	7810	7818	7825	7832	7839	7846
61	7853	7860	7868	7875	7882	7889	7896	7903	7910	7917
62	7924	7931	7938	7945	7952	7959	7966	7973	7980	7987
63	7993	8000	8007	8014	8021	8028	8035	8041	8048	8055
64	8062	8069	8075	8082	8089	8096	8102	8109	8116	8122
65	8129	8136	8142	8149	8156	8162	8169	8176	8182	8189
66	8195	8202	8209	8215	8222	8228	8235	8241	8248	8254
67	8261	8267	8274	8280	8287	8293	8299	8306	8312	8319
68	8325	8331	8338	8344	8351	8357	8363	8370	8376	8382
69	8388	8395	8401	8407	8414	8420	8426	8432	8439	8445
70	8451	8457	8463	8470	8476	8482	8488	8494	8500	8506
71	8513	8519	8525	8531	8537	8543	8549	8555	8561	8567
72	8573	8579	8585	8591	8597	8603	8609	8615	8621	8627
73	8633	8639	8645	8651	8657	8663	8669	8675	8681	8686
74	8692	8698	8704	8710	8716	8722	8727	8733	8739	8745
75	8751	8756	8762	8768	8774	8779	8785	8791	8797	8802
76	8808	8814	8820	8825	8831	8837	8842	8848	8854	8859
77	8865	8871	8876	8882	8887	8893	8899	8904	8910	8915
78	8921	8927	8932	8938	8943	8949	8954	8960	8965	8971
79	8976	8982	8987	8993	8998	9004	9009	9015	9020	9025
80	9031	9036	9042	9047	9053	9058	9063	9069	9074	9079
81	9085	9090	9096	9101	9106	9112	9117	9122	9128	9133
82	9138	9143	9149	9154	9159	9165	9170	9175	9180	9186
83	9191	9196	9201	9206	9212	9217	9222	9227	9232	9238
84	9243	9248	9253	9258	9263	9269	9274	9279	9284	9289
85	9294	9299	9304	9309	9315	9320	9325	9330	9335	9340
86	9345	9350	9355	9360	9365	9370	9375	9380	9385	9390
87	9395	9400	9405	9410	9415	9420	9425	9430	9435	9440
88	9445	9450	9455	9460	9465	9469	9474	9479	9484	9489
89	9494	9499	9504	9509	9513	9518	9523	9528	9533	9538
90	9542	9547	9552	9557	9562	9566	9571	9576	9581	9586
91	9590	9595	9600	9605	9609	9614	9619	9624	9628	9633
92	9638	9643	9647	9652	9657	9661	9666	9671	9675	9680
93	9685	9689	9694	9699	9703	9708	9713	9717	9722	9727
94	9731	9736	9741	9745	9750	9754	9759	9763	9768	9773
95	9777	9782	9786	9791	9795	9800	9805	9809	9814	9818
96	9823	9827	9832	9836	9841	9845	9850	9854	9859	9863
97	9868	9872	9877	9881	9886	9890	9894	9899	9903	9908
98	9912	9917	9921	9926	9930	9934	9939	9943	9948	9952
99	9956	9961	9965	9969	9974	9978	9983	9987	9991	9996

4.   Calculations with Logarithms

At one time or another most of us learned to use *logarithm tables* similar to those shown above. Historically, logarithms were developed as aids to numerical computation, and as soon as we learned to raise numbers to powers and to extract roots we found that "log tables" became a practical necessity. Many of you, however, have probably not used a log table in years. It is easy to interpret this as a reflection on the value of log tables in solving business problems; but the fact is, the need for log tables depends largely on the kind of mathematics one uses. Expressions involving roots and powers just do not arise in arithmetic. They arise only in the process of using more advanced mathematics. This is the reason for reviewing the concept of logarithms earlier in this chapter and for including a review of the use of log tables here.

In Section 2.4, you recall, we emphasized the fact that *logarithms* are just *exponents* of numbers to which other numbers called *bases* must be raised to produce the original number. For instance, the logarithm of the number 64 is just the exponent to which, if we use a base of 4, 4 must be raised to give us 64 again. In other words $\log_4 64 = 3$ because $4^3 = 64$. You will notice, however, in Section 2.4 we chose as a base whatever number would be most helpful in accomplishing the purpose we had in mind. For instance, in "taking logs of both sides" of the equation $2^x = N$ we used the base 2; i.e., $\log_2 (2^x) = \log_2 N$. The reason, of course, is that since $\log_2 (2^x) = x$, we end up with the desired equation $x = \log_2 N$. If we know the value of N and wish to evaluate x, however, we are apt to run into a little difficulty since tables of logarithms to the base 2 are not readily available. Let us assume for the sake of illustration that we have instead a table of logarithms to the base b available. How can we use this to help us evaluate x? The answer is to take logs on both sides to the base b to begin with. This is essentially what we do when we use "log tables" to solve an equation like this for x. In the balance of this section we will see how this is done.

Although logarithm tables could be constructed choosing any number as the base, there are two bases in common use:

1. *Common logarithms* to the base 10
   (These are indicated as log_{10} or simply log with the base 10 omitted but understood.)
2. *Natural logarithms* to the base e ($e = 2.7182 \ldots$)
   (These are indicated by log_e and sometimes by *ln.*)

In working with computers two other bases are in common use in coding systems and machine language: the base 2 (binary system) and the base 8 (octal system).

We shall confine our attention here to common logarithms (the same basic rules apply regardless of the base, by the way) and mention natural logarithms only briefly. Natural logarithms arise frequently in calculus. The base e is a constant and it represents the limit which the expression $(1 + \frac{1}{x})^x$ approaches as x becomes very large. This can be illustrated as follows:

$$\text{If } x = 2, \left(1 + \frac{1}{x}\right)^x = \left(\frac{3}{2}\right)^2 = 2.250.$$

$$\text{If } x = 10, \left(1 + \frac{1}{x}\right)^x = (1.1)^{10} = 2.594.$$

$$\text{If } x = 1,000, \left(1 + \frac{1}{x}\right)^x = (1.001)^{1,000} = 2.717.$$

As x gets infinitely large the expression $\left(1 + \frac{1}{x}\right)^x$ equals 2.7182 . . . Using symbols the statement above is written:

$$\lim_{x \to \infty} \left(1 + \frac{1}{x}\right)^x = e.$$

We shall return to $\log_e$ in Chapters 5 and 6.

The chief advantage of using logarithms is that being exponents they obey the laws of exponents. This allows us to multiply numbers by simply adding their logarithms, to raise numbers to powers by multiplying their logarithms, etc.

In using logarithms it is essential that we first consider the construction of the table of common logarithms (log tables). The table contains the logarithms of numbers between 1 and 10 only, but from this basic data logarithms of all other (positive) numbers can readily be found. The table, itself, contains no decimal points, but a decimal point is understood to precede all the numbers in the body of the table (the logarithms) and to exist between the two numbers in the column marked N. For instance, the first number under N (10) is understood to be 1.0. The first logarithm other than 0 (listed in the first row, second column as 0043) is understood to be .0043.

Notice that the logarithms start with 0 and go up to 1 (actually .9996 is the last logarithm in the table.) This corresponds to the exponential rules mentioned earlier, namely:

$$\begin{array}{lll} a^0 = 1 & 10^0 = 1 & \log 1 = 0 \\ a^1 = a & 10^1 = 10 & \log 10 = 1. \end{array}$$

Using the table to look up the logarithm of a number is illustrated in the examples below.

Example:

Find the common logarithm of 3.

1. Read in column *N* down to 30 and over to 0.

$$\log 3 = .4771$$

 24. Find the log of 7.

Answer: _____

Multiplying two numbers is equivalent to adding their logarithms.
This corresponds to the following exponential rule:

$$(10^a)(10^b) = 10^{a+b}$$
$$\log (xy) = \log x + \log y.$$

There are two ways in which this rule is frequently used. The first is in the process of finding logarithms of numbers other than those between 1 and 10.

Example:

Find the log of 525.

1. First convert 525 into two factors such that one factor is a number between 1 and 10.
2. $525 = 5.25(10^2)$
   The form of expressing numbers as shown above is called *scientific notation*.
3. $\log (5.25)(10^2) = \log 5.25 + \log 10^2$
4. $\log 5.25 = .7202$
   (Read *N* down to 52 and over to column marked 5)
5. $\log 10^2 = 2$ (by definition)
6. $\log (5.25)(10^2) = 2 + .7202 = 2.7202$
   or $\log 525 = 2.7202$.

Note that log 525 has two parts, 2 and .7202. The 2 represents the power of 10 in 10^2 and is called the *characteristic* of the logarithm. The log of 5.25 or .7202 is called the *mantissa* of the logarithm.

 25. Find the log of 715.

Answer: _____.

The *mantissa* is _____.

The *characteristic* is _____.

The second use of the multiplication (log addition) rule occurs in actually multiplying two numbers.

Example:

Use logarithms to multiply 3.75(302).

1. log (3.75)(302) = log 3.75 + log 3.02 + log 10^2

2. log 3.75 = 0.5740
   log 3.02 = 0.4800
   log 10^2 = 2.0
   _____
         3.0540

3. log (3.75) (302) = 3.0540

4. 3.0540 is the logarithm of the desired number. If x is the desired number, then $x = 10^{3.0540}$. To find the value of x we must take the *antilog* of 3.0540.

5. Finding the *antilog* is the reverse of the process of finding the logarithm. The steps are as follows:

   a. Find the logs from the table that bracket the mantissa .0540.
   log 1.14 = .0569
   log 1.13 = .0531

   b. .0569 − .0531 = .0038
   .0540 − .0531 = .0009

   c. The computation above indicates that the desired number can be approximated as lying 9/38 (or .24) of the range from 1.13 up to 1.14.

   d. Thus, from the *mantissa* we have found that one factor of the desired number is 1.1324.

   e. The *characteristic* (3) indicates the location of the demical point.
   1.1324 x 10^3 = 1,132.4

6. The answer, therefore, is 3.75(302) = 1,132.4.

   (Performing the actual multiplication produces the answer 1,132.5. Comparing this to the answer found using logarithms, it can be seen that the logarithm method is a good approximation of the result achieved by direct multiplication. For more accurate computations, larger log tables can be used.)

 26. Use logarithms to evaluate 3 times 4. Answer _____

These log tables can be used directly to find the logarithms of numbers having three significant digits such as 34.1, 341.0, 34,100, etc. To find the logarithm of a number having four or more significant digits requires an approximation method called *interpolation*.

Example:

log 6.534 = ?

1. log 6.54 = .8156
   log 6.53 = .8149
2. .8156 − .8149 = .0007
3. Since 6.534 lies 4/10 of the way between 6.53 and 6.54, the desired logarithm is approximated as lying 4/10 of the range between .8156 and .8149, and since the range is .0007 then 4/10(.0007) = .00028 or .0003.
4. The desired logarithm then is .8149 + .0003 = .8152.
5. Thus, log 6.534 = .8152.

Note that the process of interpolation shown above is similar to the method used to find the antilog illustrated in step 5 of the previous example.

 27. log 7.085 = ?   Answer _____

In finding logarithms of numbers < 1, the characteristic is a negative number. For instance, log .06 = log 6 + log 10^{-2}. In this case the characteristic is − 2, log 10^{-2} = − 2. In writing a logarithm with a negative characteristic, it is necessary to indicate that the minus sign applies only to the characteristic and not the mantissa. The following example illustrates the method used to keep this distinction clear.

Example:
$$\log .06 = \,?$$
1. log .06 = log 6 + log 10^{-2}
2. log 6 = .7782, log 10^{-2} = − 2
3. log .06 = .7782 − 2.

It is sometimes more convenient to write this as 8.7782 − 10 or 18.7782 − 20, etc., for reasons that will be illustrated shortly. All three methods are equivalent, of course.

 28. log .0034 = ?   Answer _____

Dividing two numbers is equivalent to subtracting their logarithms. This corresponds to the following exponential rule:

$$10^a \div 10^b = 10^{a-b}$$
$$\log \left(\frac{x}{y}\right) = \log x - \log y.$$

Example:

$$\log \left(\frac{3.5}{108}\right) = ?$$

1. $\log \left(\frac{3.5}{108}\right) = \log 3.5 - \log 108$

   $= \log 3.5 - (\log 1.08 + \log 10^2)$

2. $\log 3.5 = .5441$
   $\log 108 = \log 1.08 + 2 = 2.0334$

3. $\log 3.5 - \log 108 = .5441 - 2.0334$

4. In order to perform the indicated subtraction, it is convenient to write .5441 as 10.5441 − 10 as was illustrated earlier. The purpose of this is to indicate clearly that the negative sign applies only to the characteristic and not the mantissa.

5. The indicated subtraction is then performed as follows:

$$\begin{array}{r} 10.5441 - 10 \\ 2.0334 \\ \hline 8.5107 - 10 \end{array}$$

6. Hence, $\log \left(\frac{3.5}{108}\right) = 8.5107 - 10$ or $.5107 - 2$.

   (Note: .5107 is the mantissa and the characteristic is −2. If the antilog is taken, the −2 indicates that the result is to be multiplied by 10^{-2} or 1/100.)

 29. Find $\log \left(\frac{8}{4}\right)$ using log subtraction. Answer _____

Raising a number to a power is equivalent to multiplying the logarithm. The corresponding exponential rule is:

$$(10^a)^b = 10^{ab}$$
$$\log (x^y) = y \log x.$$

Example:

$$\log (416)^2 = ?$$

1. $\log (416)^2 = 2 \log 416 = 2 (\log 4.16 + 2)$

2. $\log 4.16 = .6191$
   $\log 416 = 2.6191$

3. $\log (416)^2 = 2(2.6191) = 5.2382$.

 30. $\log (.5)^3 = ?$ Answer _____

Extracting the root of a number is equivalent to dividing the logarithm (or multiplying by a fractional exponent).

$$\sqrt[b]{10^a} = 10^{a/b}$$

$$\log \sqrt[y]{x} = \frac{1}{y} \log x.$$

Example:

$$\log \sqrt[3]{8} = \text{?}$$

1. $\log \sqrt[3]{8} = \dfrac{1}{3} \log 8$

2. $\log 8 = .9031$

3. $\log \sqrt[3]{8} = \dfrac{.9031}{3} = .3010.$

 31. As shown above, $\log \sqrt[3]{8} = .3010.$ Evaluate $\sqrt[3]{8}$ by taking the antilog of .3010.

Answer _____

The following two additional points regarding logarithms have not as yet been mentioned:

1. Logarithms *cannot* be used in performing addition and subtraction of numbers.

2. Negative numbers *do not* have logarithms. (It does not follow that negative logarithms do not occur. Recall that logarithms of numbers between 0 and 1 have negative characteristics.) In dealing with negative numbers the signs must be ignored until the negative factor has been completely evaluated. The sign is then considered from that point through to the final result.

At this point, having covered all of the basic rules, let us apply them to a problem. Try to follow each step of the solution.

Example:

$$\text{Evaluate } \sqrt[3]{\frac{43.6(1.008)}{.735(937.6)}}.$$

1. $\log 43.6 = 1.6395$

2. $\log 1.008 = .0034$ (interpolation required)

3. $\log .735 = 9.8663 - 10$ (note characteristic is -1)

4. $\log 937.6 = 2.9719$ (interpolation required)

5. log of the numerator =
   $\log 43.6 + \log 1.008 =$ (multiplication rule)
   $1.6395 + .0034 \quad = \quad 1.6429$

6. log of the denominator =
   $\log .735 + \log 937.6 \quad =$ (multiplication rule)
   $9.8663 - 10 + 2.9719 \quad =$
   $12.8382 - 10 \qquad\quad = 2.8382$

7. log of whole fraction under radical =
   1.6429 − 2.8382   =   (division rule)
   11.6429 − 10 − 2.8382   = 8.8047 − 10

8. log of whole expression =
   $\dfrac{1}{3}$ (8.8047 − 10)   =   (root extraction rule)

   Note: since 3 will not divide evenly into 10 change
   8.8047 − 10 to 28.8047 − 30.

   $\dfrac{1}{3}$(28.8047 − 30) = 9.6015 − 10

9. Take the antilog of 9.6015 − 10
   antilog 9.6015 − 10 =   (interpolation required)
   3.995 x 10^{-1} = .3995

10. $\sqrt[3]{\dfrac{43.6(1.008)}{.735(937.6)}}$ = .3995.

 32. Evaluate $\sqrt[3]{(2.46)^2}$ Answer _____

33.[4] Suppose your monthly mortgage payment is R dollars. You
are considering paying the mortgage off early, hopefully, to
have it paid off before the children get to college. You can
afford to raise your monthly payment to R' and wish to know
how long it will take to pay off the mortgage at this new
higher payment rate. To find out, plug *your* numbers into
the following equation:

$$n \log (1 + i) = \log \left(\frac{-R'}{Pi - R'} \right)$$

and solve for n.

R' = the contemplated monthly payment rate.

i = interest rate of your mortgage on a monthly basis

(5% mortgage = $\dfrac{.05}{12}$ = .00417)

P = principal balance as of your last monthly payment

$$P = (R) \left[\frac{(1 + i)^{n'} - 1}{i(1 + i)^{n'}} \right].$$

(If you do not know what P is, use the above formula
first. In this formula n' = total number of monthly
payments to go on your present mortgage.)

n = the answer (in months to go).

---

[4] Optional exercise. (Disclaimer: The authors do not guarantee that your banker
will agree with your answer.)

CHAPTER **5**

Relationships between Variables

1. Introduction

1.1 RELATED VARIABLES

If we reduce costs we affect profits and possibly influence pricing, competitive position, etc. Reducing inventory has an impact on investment, profitability, floor space, ability to meet shipments. . . . And so it goes. Each decision or action sets off complex chain reactions affecting *related variables*.

Such relationships are always difficult and sometimes impossible to track. In the first place there are many more variables to consider than we are capable of dealing with at one time. Furthermore, many of the relationships are not fully understood; they are subject to outside or random influences beyond our understanding or control.

Generally we cope with the problem of making decisions in the face of such uncertainty by conducting subconscious experiments—better known as trial and error. We also gain knowledge from others conducting similar experiments.

In this chapter we shall consider some *statistical methods* for coping with such uncertainties—methods that can greatly extend our ability to deal with many variables and, at the same time, measure the degree of influence being exerted by the random factors—those that we do not fully comprehend.

1.2 UNIVARIATE VERSUS BIVARIATE DATA

In Chapters 2 and 3 we were principally concerned with *univariate* data; that is, data representing observed values of a single variable. We noted how univariate data could be conveniently summarized, and how we could improve our understanding of the process giving rise to the data through the use of graphs, averages, and the standard deviation.

In this chapter, since we are concerned with "relationships" between variables, attention will focus on *multivariate* data. For illustration purposes we will use *bivariate* data, the special multivariate case in which there are two variables of interest.

To help clarify the differences between univariate and multivariate data, consider the following example:

As a follow-up to a recently conducted attitude survey, Employee Relations was investigating areas of expressed dissatisfaction. Related to this was a recent request from the Manager–Employee Practices that the Information Systems people provide him with data regarding ages and salaries of the Department's 260 exempt employees. The information was rapidly extracted from the Personnel Accounting file accessible to the computer. It was summarized and presented as follows:

Age	No. of Exempt Employees
20–30	49
30–40	73
40–50	72
50–60	41
60 and over	25
	260

Salary	No. of Exempt Employees
$ 5,000– 7,000	78
7,000– 9,000	63
9,000–11,000	50
11,000–13,000	38
13,000–15,000	19
15,000 and over	12
	260

A quick glance at these summaries and the Manager–Employee Practices complained that the information was *useless!* "For instance," he questioned, "how can I tell from this that the 12 people making over $15,000 aren't all 20 years old?"

The Manager-Employee Practices may not have been as specific in his request as he might have been, but he was certainly correct in implying that there was little he could learn about the *relationship* between age and salary from the data presented. He was given two univariate frequency distributions when his problem called for bivariate data. The data as furnished was equivalent to presenting him with the following table:

| Age | Salary | | | | | | |
	$5,000– 7,000	7,000– 9,000	9,000– 11,000	11,000– 13,000	13,000– 15,000	15,000 & Over	Total
20–30							49
30–40							73
40–50							72
50–60							41
60 & over							260
Total . . .	78	63	50	38	19	12	260

The missing figures in the middle of the table make the difference between two univariate distributions and a single bivariate distribution. Had the problem been identified properly and the data accumulated accordingly, it would have been *cross-classified*. That is, the table would reveal the *joint occurrence* of age and salary within each of the 30 cells. At this point, however, the missing figures cannot be determined from the information available, since there are many ways in which figures can be inserted in the cells and still satisfy the totals of each row and column. The computer file had to be searched again in order to produce the bivariate frequency distribution shown in the following table. But from this the Manager-Employee Practices could see at a glance that no one making $15,000 or more was 20 years old. As a matter of fact, two thirds of the people in this salary bracket were 50 or older.

| Age | Salary | | | | | | |
	$5,000– 7,000	7,000– 9,000	9,000– 11,000	11,000– 13,000	13,000– 15,000	15,000 & over	Total
20–30	36	10	3	–0–	–0–	–0–	49
30–40	20	22	16	12	2	1	73
40–50	14	21	15	14	5	3	72
50–60	6	7	9	6	8	5	41
60 & over	2	3	7	6	4	3	25
Total . . .	78	63	50	38	19	12	260

1.3 ASSOCIATION AND ESTIMATING

If knowledge of one variable provides no information whatsoever about a second variable, little or no *association* (relationship) exists between the two variables. For example, knowing the drawing number assigned to a part by Engineering provides no information concerning the direct labor required to make the part. At the other extreme, when knowledge of one variable reveals all one can know about the other variable, perfect association exists. For instance, if 100 units are sold and the price is known to be $10 per unit, then net revenue is also known or easily determined. (This is an example of a functional relationship—the kind of relationship discussed in Chapter 4.) Many practical business problems, however, involve some intermediate degree of association between these extremes.

The main concern in the statistical analysis of bivariate data is to discover and measure the degree of association between variables. Once the nature of the association is understood and if the degree of association is high, then information concerning one variable can greatly improve one's ability to estimate or predict the second variable.

Not all cases of bivariate analysis necessarily involve estimating or predicting. For example, in the preceding paragraph the matter of concern was association between age and salary. From the data it could be observed that on the average the lower-paid employees tended to be younger, etc. The matter of association in this case would probably not be pursued further. The problem was simply one of observing what existed, and for this purpose the two-dimensional table served quite well.

Not all matters are so easily disposed of. Suppose the Manager-Budgets and Measurements has reason to believe that this month's direct labor input and next month's shop cost of output are very closely related. It would hardly be adequate for purposes of estimating next month's shop cost to know that if direct labor is increased so will next month's shop cost of output, on the average. Enough important decisions are based on such estimates to warrant a more thorough analysis into the nature and degree of the relationship between these two variables. It may be found that direct labor input provides an excellent basis for predicting shop cost of output one month hence.

1.4 ASSOCIATION: NATURE AND DEGREE

In this chapter we will illustrate two closely related aspects of bivariate analysis. The first is *regression analysis* which attempts to establish the *nature of the association* between variables. The second is *correlation* which is concerned with *degree of association* between variables.

In regression analysis, association is determined in the form of a mathematical equation. Such an equation provides the ability to predict one variable on the basis of knowledge of the other variable. The variable about which knowledge is available (or can be obtained) is called the *independent variable;* the variable whose value is to be predicted is called the *dependent variable.*

Correlation is concerned with determining and expressing the degree (or closeness) of the relationship between variables. In this case the matter of which variable to consider as independent and which to consider as dependent is inconsequential. The reason for this is that correlation can exist even though the two variables do not affect one another. Instead they may both be jointly affected by some (the same) external force. For example, there may be a high degree of correlation between the level of the water table and the wheat crop in a certain area. These variables are related only by the fact that both are influenced by the same external factor, i.e., rainfall. In contrast, in regression analysis we imply (but cannot prove) a causal relationship, e.g., the increase in last month's direct labor in some way contributed to the increase in this month's shop cost of output. This, however, is a subtle distinction in the use of the two terms that need not be of great concern to us at the moment; for, as we shall soon see, the same statistical investigation may well require both correlation and regression analysis.

Relationships between variables may be *linear* or *curvilinear.* By *linear* we mean that the relationship can be described graphically by a straight line. When a curve best describes the relationship, the relationship is said to be *curvilinear.* We shall consider only linear relationships in this chapter. However, the latter part of this chapter deals with ways in which certain curvilinear relationships commonly found in business can be mathematically transformed into linear relationships, thus making them amenable to the methods described under the heading of linear regression.

2. Regression Analysis

2.1 THE SCATTER DIAGRAM

There are several ways in which bivariate data can be organized to increase its usefulness. One way was illustrated in the age-salary example in section 1.2. This was a bivariate frequency distribution table. Another way, and one that is particularly useful in gaining a general impression about association, is the *scatter diagram*. The scatter diagram is very easy to construct. Each observation is plotted as a point on a graph having each of the variables as one of the axes. The following example illustrates the method of constructing a scatter diagram:

Glummer rings are always made to order. The cost estimator has been using the value of $40 per ring as the basis for estimating cost. His estimates, however, have not been very accurate. One reason, he thought, might be that the unit cost is related to the order quantity. To check out this theory, he compiled actual costs for all glummer ring orders for the last six months. He then plotted the points on a piece of graph paper as follows:

Order Quantity	Total Cost
30	1,200
48	1,610
35	1,400
45	1,650
40	1,600
53	1,760
25	1,300
33	1,305
39	1,500
45	1,500

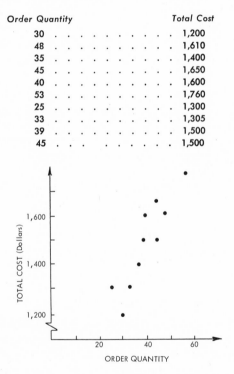

The cost estimator may or may not have known that his diagram is called a "scatter diagram," but chances are he recognized immediately how he could make good use of it in estimating the cost of glummer rings.

1. Suppose you were the cost estimator and had just received a request to quote on a new order for 40 rings. By inspection

of the scatter diagram what would you estimate total cost to be?

Answer _____

The scatter diagram reveals several useful bits of information. The first is whether or not a simple relationship exists.

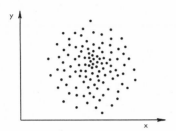

In this diagram, for instance, there is little evidence of association. It appears as though each variable is scattered about its own arithmetic mean with the variation in one variable quite independent of the values of the other. This is prima-facie evidence that further analysis, at least without considering more complex relationships involving additional variables, would be fruitless.

The following scatter diagram, on the other hand, *does* show evidence of association:

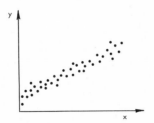

In addition, it reveals the direction of the relationship—the path of the points—which, in turn, is suggestive of the kind of mathematical equation by which the relationship might best be expressed. In this case, it appears to be a straight line, although it might well have been a curved line indicating a curvilinear relationship.

The diagram also indicates the closeness of the points to the imaginary line or curve formed by the points. This provides an indication of the degree of association. In the following diagram a possible curvilinear relationship is suggested, but the degree of association may not be clear enough to warrant further analysis.

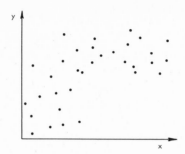

The statistician, in effect, uses the scatter diagram much like a cat uses whiskers—to feel his way. It gives him a general impression of the relationship and it provides a basis for anticipating the results of regression and correlation analysis.

 2. In the space provided draw a scatter diagram of the following data:

Sales x (000)	Accounts Receivable y (000)
$110	$108
127	122
105	109
143	134
160	150
152	145

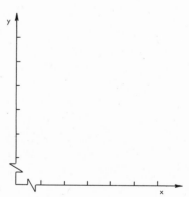

What kind of relationship would you anticipate?
Circle One
Linear   Curvilinear
What degree of association would you expect?
Circle One
Close   Not so close

2.2   LINE OF REGRESSION

Merely looking at the points on a scatter diagram is not a very precise way of defining the relationship between two variables. A much more practical way is to express the relationship by means of a mathematical equation. The simplest equation for expressing relationships is the linear or straight-line equation. Many relationships can, in fact, be satisfactorily approximated by straight lines.

From Chapter 4 you may recall that the straight-line equation takes the form $y = a + bx$, in which b is the slope of the line and a is the y-intercept. y is usually the dependent variable (or the variable to be predicted) and x is the independent variable. In regression analysis, values for x and y are known (this is the bivariate data with which one begins such an analysis.) The object of performing the analysis is to determine the values for a and b. Once values for a and b are determined, they become the constants in the resulting "predicting equation."

There are several ways of "fitting" a straight line to a set of bivariate data. The easiest way is to take a straight edge, move it around a little until you think it "looks about right," and draw the line. Once the line is drawn, its slope and the y-intercept can be determined and thus it is possible to express the equation. This method, better known as the "eyeball method," might be good enough; but how can we be sure? If we were to repeat the same procedure using the same data, would we draw the same line? With a little more "jockeying around," could we get a better fit? And how will we know when the fit is better?

An easy way around these problems, of course, is to conclude that fitting the line is "a matter of judgment." But all this does is postpone facing the issue until the first argument over whose judgment is better. The simple idea that one line can fit the data better than another implies a criterion against which "goodness" of fit ought to be measured. A young German mathematician named Gauss was eighteen years old when he concluded that the "best line" ought to represent the "most probable" values that could be inferred from the available data. On this basis he developed the *method of least squares* which, in mathematical terms, states that the line of "best fit" (also called the *line of regression*) is the line that will minimize the sum of the squared vertical distances from each point to the line. The scatter diagram on the following page will help clarify this criterion.

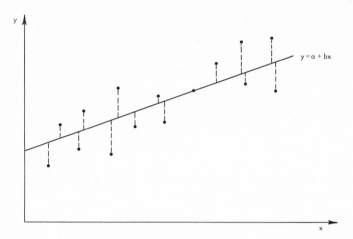

If $y = a + bx$ is the line of "best fit," the vertical distances from each point to the line (shown by the dotted lines), if squared and added together, will result in a total that is less than that achieved by repeating the same process using any *other* line. (Note the similarity of this idea to that in Chapter 3, where it was stated that the sum of the squares of the deviations of a set of numbers about another number was a minimum when that other number was the arithmetic mean.)

The regression line (or least squares line, or line of best fit) is found by substituting values for Σy, Σx, Σxy, and Σx^2 in the following two equations:

$$\Sigma y = Na + b\Sigma x$$
$$\Sigma xy = a\Sigma x + b\Sigma x^2.$$

These two equations, called *normal equations*,[1] may then be solved as simultaneous equations for the two remaining unknowns, a and b; or, to avoid having to solve the simultaneous equations on each occasion, we can use the general simultaneous solution for a and b found in Chapter 4. In this way we can get a and b directly. In Chapter 4, page 95, we found:

$$a = \frac{\Sigma y}{N} - \frac{b\Sigma x}{N}$$
$$b = \frac{N\Sigma xy - \Sigma x\Sigma y}{N\Sigma x^2 - (\Sigma x)^2}.$$

"N" in the above formulas represents the total number of observa-

---

[1] The normal equations are usually derived using methods from the calculus that will be described in Chapter 6. For this reason their derivation is not included here.

tions—in this case, bivariate observations. Each of the "N" obser-vations provides a value for the variable x and a corresponding value for the variable y.

At this point the addition of some parentheses to the formula for b will help us keep track of the order in which the arithmetic opera-tions involving the "Σ" terms are to be performed. For example, how is the term Σxy evaluated? Are the individual values of x and y added separately and then their sums multiplied? Or are corre-sponding values for x and y multiplied together first before summing their products? Of these two the latter is intended and parentheses, $\Sigma(xy)$, help make this clear. Likewise, the term Σx^2 is clarified by placing parentheses around x^2, $\Sigma(x^2)$, to help emphasize the fact that the individual x values are squared before the squares are summed. Taking the sum of the x values and then squaring would be incorrect. With appropriate parentheses added the formula for b looks as follows:

$$b = \frac{N\Sigma(xy) - (\Sigma x)(\Sigma y)}{N\Sigma(x^2) - (\Sigma x)^2}.$$

Using these two formulas, let us now fit a regression line to the following simplified data:

x	y
1	1
2	2
3	4
4	3
5	5

The first step is to construct a table that will simplify the process of collecting the information required to determine the coefficients a and b. Only two additional columns are required, xy and x^2.

x	y	xy	x^2
1	1	1	1
2	2	4	4
3	4	12	9
4	3	12	16
5	5	25	25
$\Sigma x = 15$	$\Sigma y = 15$	$\Sigma(xy) = 54$	$\Sigma(x^2) = 55$

The sum of each of the columns above provides us with a numerical value which we can now use in the formulas for a and b in place of the terms involving Σ's.

$$b = \frac{N\Sigma(xy) - (\Sigma x)(\Sigma y)}{N\Sigma(x^2) - (\Sigma x)^2}$$

$$= \frac{5(54) - (15)(15)}{5(55) - (15)^2}$$

$$= \frac{45}{50} = .9,$$

$$a = \frac{\Sigma y}{N} - b\frac{\Sigma x}{N}$$

$$= \frac{15}{5} - .9\left(\frac{15}{5}\right)$$

$$= 3 - 2.7 = .3.$$

Therefore, the regression equation is:

$$y = a + bx = .3 + .9x.$$

The graph of this equation can be drawn by arbitrarily selecting at least two values for the independent variable, x, and calculating the corresponding values for the dependent variable, y. For example, when $x = 0$, $y = .3 + .9(0) = .3$, and when $x = 3$, $y = .3 + .9(3) = 3.0$. We can now connect these two points $(x = 0, y = .3)$ and $(x = 3, y = 3.0)$ with a straight line. The equation of this line is $y = .3 + .9x$, since each pair of values of x and y that satisfy the equation represents a point on the graph of the line.

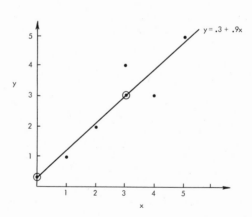

3. Using "regression analysis," provide the cost estimator in the glummer ring problem with an estimating equation. (The basic data, including a partially completed table, is provided on the following page.)

Answer _____

Order Qty. x	Total Cost y	xy	x^2
30	1,200	36,000	900
48	1,610	77,280	2,304
35	1,400	49,000	1,225
45	1,650	74,250	2,025
40	1,600	64,000	1,600
53	1,760	93,280	2,809
25	1,300	32,500	625
33	1,305	_____	____
39	1,500	_____	____
45	1,500	_____	____

4. Using the equation derived above, estimate the cost of a new order for 40 glummer rings.

Answer _____

(How does this estimate compare with your "eyeball" estimate in Section 2.1?)

2.3 REGRESSION ANALYSIS AND BUSINESS PROBLEMS

Regression analysis is applied to a set of data for the purpose of determining the nature of the relationship between variables. From a business point of view, interest in regression analysis arises from the continuing need to base plans on predictions or estimates of future events. The selection of the variables upon which to base an analysis presumes considerable knowledge of the subject matter. As useful as regression analysis is, it cannot create intelligence. The starting point must always be an intelligent "guess" regarding possible fruitful relationships to investigate. The results of analysis tell us how good our guesses were—whether, in fact, the variables are related. The accountant, for instance, wishing to predict balances in accounts like Sundry Creditors, Vacations and Payrolls Accrued, etc., would look for relationships with Employment or Direct Labor, not with such variables as Direct Material, etc.

The statistical determination of a relationship does not indicate the reason, it merely establishes the fact. It is another matter entirely to answer the next logical question, i.e., "why" the variables are related. In this sense, regression analysis is an experimental process. While it may be (and, in fact, has been) used to indicate a relationship between smoking and lung cancer, understanding why such a relationship exists is a matter beyond the scope of regression analysis. In using regression analysis, we assert a causal relationship between the dependent and independent variable. The results can reinforce this assertion, but regression analysis alone cannot prove cause and effect. This can be appreciated by recognizing the possibility of selecting two sets of observations at random and finding that they exhibit a relationship.

For example, a study once conducted in Indiana showed a close relationship over the years between the salaries paid to college professors and the sale of liquor in package stores. To infer from this that the professors were "drinking-up" their salary increases, however, would not only be an unfair indictment but wholly inaccurate as well. Both variables were probably responding to the same economic pressures, but using knowledge of either to predict the other would hardly be justifiable.

In the example used in section 2.2 we illustrated the general approach to regression analysis using "simple linear regression." (Simple in this context means that the prediction of the dependent variable was based on a single independent variable.) Many practical applications, however, will involve a good many more than a single independent variable. For example, in a recent application of regression analysis, a defense-oriented business used a total of four independent variables to predict Customer Receivables Account balances:

$x_1 =$ Cost Recovery Sales (with interim billing)
$x_2 =$ Cost Recovery Sales (without interim billing)
$x_3 =$ Firm Price Sales
$x_4 =$ Monthly Working Day Index

The resulting regression equation took the form:

$$y = a + b_1x_1 + b_2x_2 + b_3x_3 + b_4x_4.$$

Several variables were used here in recognition of the fact that more than one factor was affecting Customer Receivables and each of the separate factors had its own unique impact. The problem, however, is very similar to simple regression except that instead of the best fitting line, the best fitting plane is found. (Notice, however, that the plane cannot be graphed on a scatter diagram, since we cannot draw the 5-dimensional graph that is required.) The analysis in this case is the same except that it requires more equations (5 in this example) similar to the two normal equations illustrated earlier. The method is called "multiple linear regression."

In the same application, a curvilinear relationship was found as the most satisfactory means of predicting Progress Collections from Firm Price Sales. The equation took the form:

$$y = a + bx + cx^2 \qquad \text{(for a limited range of } x \text{)}.$$

In this case the best fitting *curve* is found using the least squares criterion.

Continuing in similar manner an interlocking network of predicting equations made possible the prediction of all major account balances and other significant business measures. The resulting equations were interlocking in the sense that predictions of some variables were, in turn, used to predict other variables. In other words, while related factors were piled up in interlocking fashion, they were actually peeled off one by one in the analysis.[2]

The following quotation provides a general over-all view of some of the typical applications being made of regression analysis.

A wide range of problems has been subjected to regression analysis. Fields such as crop forecasting, analysis of supply and demand, the study of consumption, market analysis, all have been notable areas for the application of the techniques of regression and correlation. The influence of varying weather conditions on the yield of crops may be effectively analyzed by regression methods. Regression studies of the influence of physical input on output have been made for potatoes, cotton, and many other crops. Procedures for estimating the value of farms on the basis of farm characteristics and other factors have proven important in levying taxes and securing loans. Economic analysis of the factors influencing prices is heavily dependent upon regression analysis. For example, a recent study has related the per capita consumption of calories per day in various countries to the national income per capita. Regression analysis has been applied to the explanation of technological change and the rate of economic development. A number of general regression studies have been made of savings, investment, and consumption, which have been significant in the field of econometrics. Individual business enterprises make numerous applications of regression methods. A major railroad predicted the number of meals to be served in the dining cars of all-Pullman trains on the basis of the number of advance reservations for seats on the train made by all passengers. A mail-order house predicted

---

[2] R. A. Knapp, "Forecasting and Measuring with Correlation Analysis," *Financial Executive,* Vol. XXXI (May, 1963), pp. 13–19.

the number of orders it would have to process in a day on the basis of the weight of the morning mail.[3]

3.   Correlation

3.1   MEASURING CORRELATION

Our concern in using regression analysis was to determine and express the relationship between two variables in the form of an equation. Such an equation was then useful in predicting a dependent variable based on knowledge of an independent variable. Before basing important decisions on such predictions, however, it is useful to know something of the *degree* (or closeness) *of the relationship* between the variables. The confidence we can place in such predictions, in fact, depends on the closeness of the relationship.

Closeness of the relationship is revealed in a qualitative sense by the closeness of the points on a scatter diagram to the regression line, but in correlation analysis we seek to measure the closeness of relationship in quantitative terms. The most important of these quantitative measures are the *coefficient of correlation* and its square, the *coefficient of determination*. Neither of these measures require identification of one variable as dependent and the other as independent. Instead, the closeness of relationship is obtained by measuring the proportion of the variation in one variable (either one) which can be "explained by" knowledge of the accompanying values of the other variable.

To understand the meaning of the term "explained by," consider the data used to illustrate the regression line in section 2.2.

x		y
1	. . . .	1
2	. . . .	2
3	. . . .	4
4	. . . .	3
5	. . . .	5

Suppose for a moment that you were asked to predict y knowing only that the past values of y had been 1, 2, 3, 4, and 5. In other words, assume that you had no information regarding the corresponding values of x.

---

[3] John I. Griffin, *Statistics, Methods and Applications* (New York: Holt, Rinehart & Winston, 1962), pp. 238–39.

Given this condition, you could do no better than to predict the arithmetic mean, i.e., $\Sigma y/n = \bar{y} = 3$. The basis for this prediction is your knowledge that the sum of the deviations is zero and that the total variance of y is a minimum when measured from the arithmetic mean as opposed to any other single value of y. These are basic properties of the arithmetic mean. Plotting a scatter diagram, this estimate would be represented by the line $y = 3$ as shown on the following diagram:

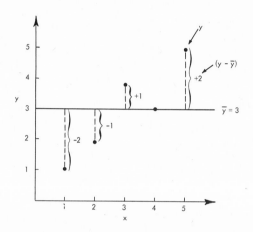

The actual deviations are shown by the dotted lines and it can be seen that $\Sigma(y - \bar{y}) = 0$, and that the total variance is

$$s^2 = \frac{\Sigma(y - \bar{y})^2}{n} = \frac{10}{5} = 2.00.$$

Now suppose that you were again asked to predict values for y, only this time *with* knowledge of the corresponding values of x. Could you, on the basis of this additional information, improve your prediction? The answer, of course, is that you could improve it considerably. In section 2.2, in fact, we found that the best estimate of y based on knowledge of x was the regression line, $y = .3 + .9x$. In other words, knowing x, we could calculate a value of y, call it y_c, that would fall on the regression line. Our prediction then would be y_c instead of $\bar{y}$. If we plot the regression line on the scatter diagram, we can now show the deviations of y from our new estimate, y_c. These deviations, $\Sigma(y - y_c)$ are shown by solid lines from y (the observed values) to y_c (the values one would calculate using the regression line) on the diagram that follows.

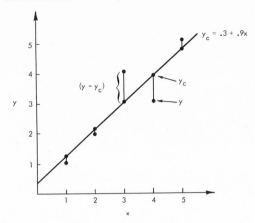

We can now compare the variance of the $(y - y_c)$ deviations with the $(y - \overline{y})$ deviations directly by showing the deviations from the mean $(\overline{y} = 3$ line$)$ as dotted lines and the deviations from the regression line as solid lines. From a visual inspection of this dia-

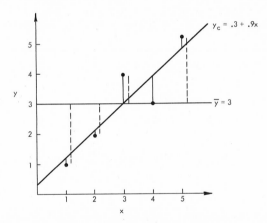

gram the solid lines are seen to be a good deal less in total than the dotted lines. As a result the variance is also a good deal less. We can check to make sure by calculating the variance of y from y_c as follows:

x	y	$y_c = .3 + .9x$	$y - y_c$	$(y - y_c)^2$
1	1	1.2	− .2	.04
2	2	2.1	− .1	.01
3	4	3.0	+1.0	1.00
4	3	3.9	.9	.81
5	5	4.8	+ .2	.04
			$\Sigma(y - y_c) = 0$	$\Sigma(y - y_c)^2 = 1.90$

$$s^2 \; (\text{using } y_c) = \frac{\Sigma(y - y_c)^2}{n} = \frac{1.9}{5} = .38.$$

Recalling that s^2 (using $\bar{y}$) $= 2.00$, we can see that a large part of the total variance has been removed. In other words, using our knowledge of values of x has helped us to "account for" or "explain" much of the total variance. Or, another way of saying the same thing, there is a high degree of correlation between x and y. If all the variation in y were explained by x, we would have *perfect* correlation. If this were the case, there would be no difference between observed values of y and the values of y (i.e., the y_c's) predicted using the regression equation. This would yield an s^2 (using y_c) of zero. The fact that s^2 (using y_c) in our example does not equal zero—and it is highly unlikely that it would in a statistical problem—indicates that there is still some variation left in y that our knowledge of x does not help to explain.

Before considering the coefficients of correlation, let us review the meaning of the terms "explained" and "unexplained" variance from a little different viewpoint. Suppose you were given the following data covering 12 observations on the variables x and y:

x	y		x	y
1	1		2	3
1	2		2	4
1	2		3	3
1	3		3	4
2	2		3	4
2	3		3	5

Based on this data let us plot four frequency histograms as follows:

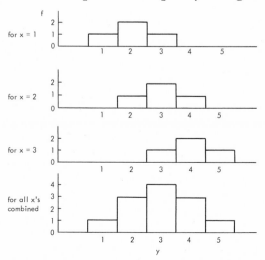

If you were now asked to guess an unknown value of y (randomly selected from among the 12), without being told the corresponding value of x, one could do no better than to guess 3, which is the mean of all the y's. The *error* one stands to make in such a guessing game is measured by the *variance* of the distribution of all the y's. In this case, s^2 (using $\bar{y}$ for all values of y) is equal to $14/12 = 1.17$. If you were now asked to guess an unknown value of y (again randomly selected from among the 12), but this time *with knowledge* of the x-value which corresponds, you would obviously guess the mean value of the distribution corresponding to that x. If you knew x were 3, you should guess $y = 4$, for example. The *error* you would make in such guesses as this is measured *not* by the total variance of all y's, but rather by the variance of the distribution of the y's corresponding to only the single value of x. In this problem the distribution of y is the same for every x; the variance of any one of these groups of four y-values is s^2 (using $\bar{y}$ corresponding to one value of x only) $= 2/4 = 0.50$. This is equivalent to s^2 (using y_c).

So *without* knowledge of x, the error variance is 1.17; *with* knowledge of x, the error variance is 0.50. We then say that knowledge of x "explains" 0.67 of the total of 1.17 and the remaining 0.50 is "unexplained by x." In the general case, when many observations are involved, the scatter diagram can be overlaid with the frequency distribution of y-values, as shown in the following diagram.

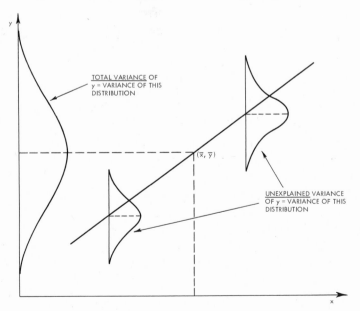

3.2 COEFFICIENTS

The two measures of correlation are called the *coefficient of correlation* and the *coefficient of determination*. They are developed as follows:

1. Let us first abbreviate s^2 (using $\bar{y}$) to s_y^2, and s^2 (using y_c) to $s_{y_c}^2$.
2. Next let us call s_y^2 the "total" variance because this is the variance in y when all values of y are considered without knowledge of corresponding values.
3. The variance that remains "unexplained" after taking values of x into consideration by regression analysis is given by $s_{y_c}^2$.
4. The variance that has been "explained" by regression analysis, therefore, must be the difference between the "total" and "unexplained" variance or $s_y^2 - s_{y_c}^2$.
5. The proportion of the "explained" to the "total" variance is

$$\frac{s_y^2 - s_{y\,c}^2}{s_y^2}.$$

This can be reduced to

$$1 - \frac{s_{y\,c}^2}{s_y^2}.$$

This latter result (above) is known as the *coefficient of determination,* and the square root of this proportion is defined as "r," the *coefficient of correlation:*

$$r = \pm \sqrt{1 - \frac{s_{y\,c}^2}{s_y^2}}.$$

From this formula one can see that in the case of *perfect correlation* $s_{y_c}^2 = 0$, which results in a value of r equal to one. In the case of *no correlation* $s_{y_c}^2$ would be just as large as s_y^2 and the resulting value of r would be zero. The coefficient of correlation, therefore, ranges from $r = -1$ to $r = +1$, with these extreme values both representing perfect correlation, but of opposite direction.

The *coefficient of determination* is a more convenient way of expressing the degree of relationship between two variables. This coefficient is the square of r and is denoted simply as r^2. The advantage of the coefficient of determination lies in the fact that it is easier to interpret because it expresses the proportion of the variance in y explained by x in terms of the relative reduction in variance. For example, if $r = .9$ then $r^2 = .81$, which is interpreted as follows: 81% of the variance in y has been explained by knowledge of x.

5. Calculate the coefficient of correlation from the sample data used in Section 2.2, i.e., $(x,y) = (1,1)$, $(2,2)$, $(3,4)$, $(4,3)$, $(5,5)$.

$$r = \underline{\hspace{4cm}}$$

6. Calculate the coefficient of determination using the same data and interpret the results.

$$r^2 = \underline{\hspace{4cm}}$$

_____

_____

In most cases regression and correlation analyses will both be required before any predictions will be made. For this reason it is convenient not to have to develop the regression equation and calculate two kinds of deviations for each individual y. This can be avoided; in fact, the *regression equation* and the *degree of correlation* can both be developed at the same time using the following expression for r:

$$r = \frac{N\Sigma xy - \Sigma x \Sigma y}{\sqrt{N\Sigma x^2 - (\Sigma x)^2} \ \sqrt{N\Sigma y^2 - (\Sigma y)^2}}$$

Using this formula, r will be positive when y values increase as x values increase and negative when y values decrease as x values increase. This explains why r was said earlier to range between values of $+ 1$ and $- 1$.

Although this equation may look more complicated than our previous expression for r, from a computational point of view, it saves a great deal of time. All the information required to find the regression equation, as well as the coefficients of determination and correlation, can be found by completing the following table:

x	y	x^2	y^2	xy
•	•	•	•	•
•	•	•	•	•
•	•	•	•	•
Σx	Σy	Σx^2	Σy^2	Σxy

7. Find the regression equation and r^2 from the following data:

x	y
5	1
4	2
3	4
2	3
1	5

3.3   THE EASY WAY

In our discussion of regression and correlation analyses you may have noted that there was a fair amount of computational work to be performed. This was true even in the greatly oversimplified sample problems we used. The computations were all simple; there were just a lot of them. In any practical problem we would, of course, have a lot more data to work with. In addition, we might have several independent variables to be considered (multiple regression). Furthermore, since this kind of analysis is largely experimental, we might also wish to explore several possible relationships. Under these circumstances, it is not difficult to see that the computational problem becomes enormous. As a result, almost all practical analysis work today is performed with the aid of computers. And almost all computers have very convenient "canned" regression and correlation programs available. Many of these programs are equipped for multiple regression analysis, and from raw data input they very rapidly produce the regression equation and measures of correlation.

4.   Curve Fitting by Least Squares

4.1   PROBLEM REDUCTION

During an oral examination for the degree of Ph.D. in Mathematics, a young doctoral candidate was asked by one of the more venerable of the assembled scholars the following unlikely question: "Assume the desk here is a stove, and that wastebasket over there is a bucket of water. Now, I ask you, how would you solve the problem of heating the water on the stove?"

The degree candidate was stunned for a moment and then replied, "Why, I guess I would pick up the bucket of water from the floor and place it on the stove."

To the candidate's surprise the old professor was visibly pleased. "Excellent, excellent!" he exclaimed. "Good bit of reasoning!"

"Now that you have solved that problem so neatly, let me ask you a more difficult one." With this the professor walked to the wastebasket, picked it up, and placed it on the table on the far side of the room.

"Suppose the bucket of water were over there. You agree, do you not, that this is a more difficult problem?"

The puzzled degree candidate managed a nod of agreement.

"Very well then, how would you solve the problem of heating the water now?"

After a moment's hesitation—"Well, I guess I would pick up the bucket of water from over there," said the candidate making a gesture in the direction of the table, "and then place it on the stove."

To this the old professor stormed, "Wrong, wrong, wrong! And you think you're a mathematician, do you? Ha! Well let me tell you, damned little progress would be made if all mathematicians went about their work the same way you went about this problem! *Reduce the difficult problem to a simpler one that you've already solved.* That's the secret to mathematical progress."

Then with a slight smile he added, "Why, any mathematician worth his salt would have known enough to move the bucket from the table to the floor first. Putting the bucket on the floor, you see, reduces the problem to one you have already solved!"

Considering the situation, the degree candidate was probably speechless at this point. And, chances are, the old professor assumed the attitude of an oracle who had just spoken. (Old professors can do this.) At any rate the point was a good one; try to reduce a complex problem to a simpler one that you already know how to solve. This is a lesson worth learning—with or without the aid of wastebaskets.

In the balance of this chapter we will apply this lesson to something a bit more practical—the fitting of a least squares line to curvilinear data. But how can we do this, you may wonder? Certainly if the path of points on a scatter diagram appears to describe a curvilinear relationship, no straight line, not even the "best-fitting" straight line, is going to produce very accurate estimates. This, of course, is true! But if we can find a way of expressing the curvilinear relationship in the form of a straight line, i.e., in a form similar to $y = a + bx$, we will have reduced the problem to a simpler one that we already know how to solve.

For many curvilinear relationships commonly encountered in business problems, this is easily accomplished by simply combining a little algebra with our newly acquired familiarity with linear regression. In the following section we will illustrate this method of fitting a least squares line to several common types of curvilinear relationships.

4.2 THE EXPONENTIAL TREND

A curvilinear relationship frequently encountered in business problems is the *exponential trend.* This is a curve characterized by the geometric progression (or decay) of values of one of the variables while values of the other variable appear to progress in arithmetic fashion. The nature of this relationship can best be described in terms of a classic example.

Roughly speaking bacteria multiply by dividing. To clarify this, each bacterium simply divides into two bacteria under the right set of conditions after a given time interval. As a result the total number of bacteria at any future time depends, first, on how many there were to start with, and further, on how many maturity time intervals have passed. At the end of the first maturity interval, of course, there would be twice as many. Each of the "twice as many" would again divide at the end of the second interval, and so on. The total number of bacteria in this process is said to be increasing geometrically, while time is progressing arithmetically. The bacteria follow an exponential *growth* trend.

A classic example of an exponential *decay* trend is the loss or decay in radiation from a radioactive isotope—the so-called "half-life" measure of the rate of decay is derived from this phenomenon.

In the business environment exponential trends fit such variables as the accumulation of money at compound interest. They are also found to describe certain short-term trends in sales and earnings (either growth or erosion). The purchase price in contracts for leased equipment and the utilization or depletion of resources under certain conditions also frequently exhibit the characteristics of exponential trends.

The general form of the equation for the exponential trend is:

$$y = ae^{bx} \qquad \text{(for growth)},$$
$$y = ae^{-bx} \qquad \text{(for decay)}.$$

Depending on the values of the constants the graphs appear roughly as shown in the following diagram:

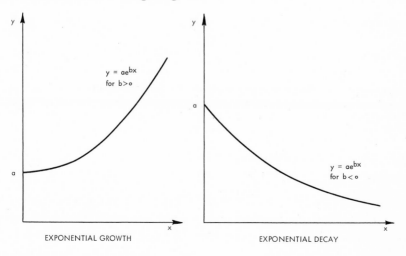

EXPONENTIAL GROWTH   EXPONENTIAL DECAY

Before we can apply the method of linear regression to data exhibiting this kind of relationship, we must first convert the equation of the curve into an equation having the form of a straight line. This can be accomplished by taking logarithms to the base 10 on both sides of the equation $y = ae^{bx}$ as follows:

$$(\log y) = (\log a) + (b \log e)x.$$

This now can be written in straight-line form if we make the following *transformation:*

Let $Y = \log y$
$\quad A = \log a$
$\quad B = b \log e \qquad\qquad (\log e = \log 2.7183 = .4343)$
$\quad X = x$

The straight line equation is then:

$$Y = A + BX.$$

From this point we can find the coefficients A and B using the least squares method described earlier. Starting with values of x and y, of course, we must first convert y into Y. The following sample data will illustrate:

$x = X$	y	$Y = \log y$	XY	X^2
1	1.6	.2041	.2041	1
2	4.5	.6532	1.3064	4
3	13.8	1.1399	3.4197	9
4	40.2	1.6042	6.4168	16
5	125.0	2.0969	10.4845	25
$\Sigma X = 15$		$\Sigma Y = 5.6983$	$\Sigma(XY) = 21.8315$	$\Sigma(X^2) = 55$

From this data we can now derive the coefficients A and B.

$$B = \frac{N\Sigma(XY) - \Sigma X\Sigma Y}{N\Sigma(X^2) - (\Sigma X)^2} = \frac{5(21.8315) - 15(5.6983)}{5(55) - (15)^2}$$

$$B = .4737$$

$$A = \frac{\Sigma Y}{N} - \frac{B\Sigma X}{N} = \frac{5.6983}{5} - \frac{.4737(15)}{5}$$

$$A = -.2814.$$

We have now found the constants A and B in the transformed straight-line equation. To put this back into exponential form, we need only compute the constants a and b by using the transformation "backwards":

$$B = b \log e, \text{ so } b = \frac{B}{\log e}$$
$$= \frac{.4737}{.4343}$$
$$\text{or } b = 1.091,$$

$$A = \log a, \text{ so } a = \text{antilog } A$$
$$= \text{antilog } (-.2814)$$
$$= \text{antilog } (9.7186 - 10)$$
$$a = 0.5231.$$

From this, we can write the equation of the exponential trend, $y = ae^{bx}$, which fits this data:

$$y = 0.5231 \, e^{1.091x}$$

One other property of the exponential trend is especially useful when it is desired to state the growth (or decay) rate of the variable y, where x is a time variable. For the equation $y = ae^{bx}$, the *growth rate* is $(e^b - 1)$, as can be seen from the following:

At time x:

$$y_x = ae^{bx}.$$

At time $x + 1$:

$$y_{x+1} = ae^{b(x+1)}$$

Increase in unit time:

$$y_{x+1} - y_x = ae^{bx+b} - ae^{bx}$$
$$= ae^b e^{bx} - ae^{bx}$$
$$= ae^{bx} (e^b - 1).$$

Relative change in unit time (or growth rate):

$$\frac{y_{x+1} - y_x}{y_x} = \frac{ae^{bx} (e^b - 1)}{ae^{bx}}$$
$$= e^b - 1.$$

In the previous example you may recall that B was found to equal .4737. You may also recall that $B = b \log e = \log (e^b)$. From this information we can compute the *growth rate* $(e^b - 1)$ in the previous example as follows:

$$B = .4737 = \log (e^b)$$
$$e^b = \text{antilog } (.4737) = 2.976$$
$$e^b - 1 = 2.976 - 1 = 1.976 \text{ or } 197.6\%.$$

 8. Check the relative growth rate of 1.976 just calculated for the example by dividing each y value of the original data by the preceding y value. The y values are given below. (Since

we are concerned with the relative growth, 1 must be subtracted from the result of the division prior to comparison with 1.976.)

$$\frac{4.5}{1.6} = \underline{\hspace{2cm}}$$

$$\frac{13.8}{4.5} = \underline{\hspace{2cm}}$$

$$\frac{40.2}{13.8} = \underline{\hspace{2cm}}$$

$$\frac{125.0}{40.2} = \underline{\hspace{2cm}}$$

Is the 1.976 a reasonable estimate of the growth rate?

Does this exercise suggest a way to test data for possible fitting with an exponential trend?

4.3　OTHER CURVE FORMS

Another curve form frequently encountered in data relating cost (or price) to volume (either of purchases or production) is described as an *hyperbola*. The equation of this curve often appears in the form:

$$y = a + \frac{b}{x}.$$

Depending on the values of the constants the general form of the *hyperbola* is as shown below. Its main characteristic is that it approaches but never reaches limiting values in both the x and y dimensions.

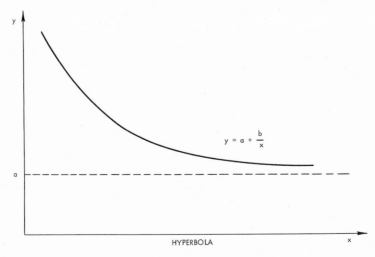

$$y = a + \frac{b}{x}$$

HYPERBOLA

The reason for the common occurrence of this relation can be recognized if we view the elements of the equation in the following terms:

Let y = unit cost (or price)
  a = variable cost per unit
  b = fixed cost
  x = number of units produced (or purchased)

This relationship states that the unit cost is equal to the variable cost, a, plus a prorata share of the fixed cost dependent on number of units. The prevalence of this type of curve stems from the widespread use of fixed and variable cost systems in industry.

The required *transformation* in this case to convert to linear form is simply:

Let $Y = y$
  $A = a$
  $B = b$
  $X = \dfrac{1}{x}$

This is now linear in $Y = A + BX$ and the required table headings are:

x	$Y = y$	$X = \dfrac{1}{x}$	XY	X^2

One final curve that we will consider is the so-called *power function*. The general equation of the power function is:

$$y = ax^b.$$

The importance of this equation in industry can be more easily recognized if the elements of the equation are interpreted as follows:

Let y = the average unit cost in producing x units
  a = the cost to produce the first unit
  x = the number of units produced
  b = a constant related to percentage reduction in cost per each additional unit produced

In other words, this is one of many variations of the "learning curve." (One widely publicized variation of the learning curve is the so-called "80 per cent airframe curve":

$$y = \frac{kn^{.678}}{.678}.$$

This particular curve, in which y is in terms of the total cost to produce n units, shows a 20 per cent reduction in unit cost every time production doubles.)

The required transformation to convert the power function to a linear form is:

$Y = \log y$
$A = \log a$
$B = b$
$X = \log x$

The linear equation, therefore, becomes $Y = A + BX$ and the required column headings are:

x	y	$X = \log x$	$Y = \log y$	XY	X^2

Practice Problem

Data covering total industry sales (in millions of dollars) of rollavator coil controls is available as follows:

Year	Total Industry Sales (10^6)
1958	19
1959	26
1960	32
1961	41
1962	49
1963	64
1964	78

A recent publication of the American Rollavator Association Economic Bureau uses this data to forecast 1967 industry sales in the amount of $101.6 million. Their forecast is based on the following equation, which they claim to have derived using linear regression techniques:

$$\text{Industry Sales} = 15.2 + 9.6\,(\text{Year}-1958).$$

In preparing back-up information to support your Department's Long-Range Forecast, you plot a graph of this data and sketch in the regression line. (Plot this line now before going on.)

Notice that the straight line seems to give a more pessimistic view of the future than you might have taken just by looking at the data. As a result you decide to fit an exponential trend, i.e., $y = ae^{bx}$, to the data to see if that describes the sales growth better than the straight line does.

Find the equation of the exponential trend that best fits this data.

Using this equation, estimate industry sales in each of the years 1958–64, and plot the curve.

Does this appear to be a better estimating equation than the straight line?

What is your 1967 forecast of industry sales for coil controls?

What is the average annual growth rate of industry sales during the period covered by the data?

CHAPTER 6

Calculus:
Mathematics of Change

1. Introduction

1.1 MATHEMATICS FOR A DYNAMIC WORLD

During the course of the centuries, mathematics has been called upon to provide solutions for problems that have arisen in various human pursuits, for which no solution was known at the time. So it was in the Renaissance period—the age of mechanics, the age of the great explorers, of gunpowder, and the printing press. And as man faced the sea with no true science of navigation, as he experimented with instruments whose intricate notions went beyond his ability to understand, and as he fired cannonballs into trajectories he had no way of describing, the need for new mathematical tools became increasingly apparent.

The mathematics inherited from preceding periods was especially inadequate for studying problems of motion. The resources that mathematics had to offer in the middle of the seventeenth century were plainly insufficient to solve the practical problems of the new dynamic world. New tools invented for the purpose of solving these new and usually aggravating problems were Analytic Geometry (by Descartes in 1637) and Calculus (independently by both Newton and Leibniz about 40 years later).

The methods of Analytic Geometry, in which algebraic equations correspond to graphs and vice versa, are in every mathematician's repertoire. The methods of the Calculus have taken all the sting out of problems involving quantities that are changing. As the science we call "business" outgrows the purely static and descriptive phase and enters the dynamic and quantitative stage, these methods will be increasingly useful. This chapter will explain the concepts of Calculus, and how they apply.

2. Basic Ideas of Calculus

2.1 RATE OF CHANGE

The ocean has made a five-mile inroad into the coastline. A disaster? Not really. After all, it took millions of years to get that far.

The population in our town has doubled. But hasn't the same thing happened to most communities? Not in a single year, it hasn't!

Costs have been reduced by 10 per cent in the past year. Great, must have had a record year. No, unfortunately! Prices were soft so earnings weren't too hot.

In each of these examples a comparison of the two related changes is called for before reaching conclusions regarding the current state of affairs. In the first case a change in distance and a change in time must be compared to realize that there is no cause for alarm. The second case clearly describes a boom town when the change in population is related to the time in which the change took place. In the final example, the reduction in costs compared to changes in selling price amounted to little or no profit improvement.

Let us now see how such comparisons can be made using formulas. Suppose, for example, that it costs $200 to bring a cold oven up to operating temperature and $15 an hour to hold it there. The cost to operate the oven at temperature therefore is:

$$C = 200 + 15(1) \qquad \text{for 1 hour}$$
$$= 200 + 15(2) \qquad \text{for 2 hours}$$
$$= 200 + 15(3) \qquad \text{for 3 hours}$$
$$\text{and so on}$$

From this we can see that cost and operating time, t, in hours are related by the following formula:

$$C = 200 + 15t.$$

Using this formula we can construct the following table:

t	Change in t	C	Change in C
0		200	
	1		15
1		215	
	1		15
2		230	
	1		15
3		245	

After the first hour of operation the change in t has been 1 hour and the change in C has been $15. The change in t and in C between the 1st and 2nd hour is likewise 1 and 15, respectively. After three hours of operation the change in t is 3 and the corresponding change in C is 45. From this we can note the following ratio representing the *rate of change* in C:

$$\frac{\text{Change in } C}{\text{Change in } t} = \frac{15}{1} = \frac{45}{3} = \$15. \text{ per hour.}$$

Using the mathematical symbol for change which is Δ (the Greek letter *delta*), a formula for the *rate of change* in cost is

$$\frac{\Delta C}{\Delta t} = 15.$$

In this example, no matter how large a change we observed, the ratio $\Delta C/\Delta t$ remained unchanged. Whether we measured the change between successive hours or between, say, the 1st and 3rd hours $\Delta C/\Delta t = 15$. What we are observing here is a characteristic of an equation whose form is already familiar—the equation of the straight line. (We shall see shortly that this ratio varies from point to point when the relationship is not linear.)

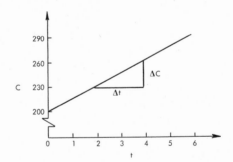

If we draw a graph of the equation $C = 200 + 15t$, we see that $\Delta C/\Delta t$ is also the *slope of the line*. This corresponds to the significance we attached earlier to the coefficient b in the general form of the equation for a straight line, $y = a + bx$. Since t and C are equivalent to x and y in the general equation and since $\Delta C/\Delta t$ equals the slope of the line, then, in general:

$$\frac{\Delta y}{\Delta x} = b = \text{slope of the line} = \text{rate of change.}$$

We can show this another way by letting r and s represent any two values for x in the equation $y = a + bx$ as follows:

x	y
r	a + br
s	a + bs

$$\Delta x = s - r \qquad \Delta y = (a + bs) - (a + br) = b(s - r)$$
$$\frac{\Delta y}{\Delta x} = \frac{b(s - r)}{(s - r)} = b.$$

1. In the equation $R = 50 - 6t$, how much will R change when t changes from $t = 1$ to $t = 3$?

Change in R: _____

How much will R change if t decreases by one unit?

Change in R: _____

What is the slope of the graph of this equation?

Slope: _____

Let us now illustrate this same concept of rate of change using a curvilinear relationship instead of a straight line. For this purpose let us use the following data that we can imagine has been extracted from an insurance rate book:

A = Insuring Age	P = Annual Premium ($) per $M of Face Value	ΔP = Changes in P (the Differences)
30	9.25	
35	10.88	1.63
40	12.97	2.09
45	15.73	2.76
50	19.29	3.56

We have included the last column on the right to show the difference or change in annual premium rate from one age to another. How would you answer the question, "How much does the annual premium change for a one-year increase in insuring age?"

There is no *one* numerical answer to this question. For example, the annual premium increases $1.63 between the ages 30 and 35; it increases a different amount ($3.56) between ages 45 and 50. In other words the rate of change of P with age A is different depending on the value of A. If we were to plot the data from the table above, the different rates of change could be seen more clearly as illustrated in the chart on the following page:

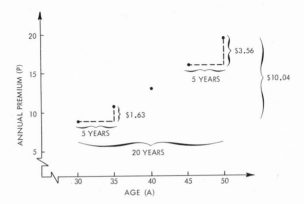

Thus, the change in premium from age 30 to age 35 is $1.63/5 or about 32 cents per year. From age 45 to age 50, on the other hand, it is $3.56/5 or about 71 cents per year. On a 20-year basis, the "average" rate of change is $10.04/20 or 50 cents per year.

From this we can see that there is no single value which will describe the rate of change in problems like this, for the rate of change itself depends on the value of the changing quantity at any particular instant. Differential Calculus aims at finding formulas for such rates of change, as we will see in a moment.

2.2 THE DERIVATIVE

Looking down at the street from one of the upper floors of a modern office building caused us to speculate recently as to the kind of questions a tour guide at, say, Rockefeller Center would be expected to answer. We concluded that it would certainly be in the public's best interest if the guide had an answer to, "What would happen if I dropped a baseball down there?" When this question is asked by the young experimental scientist—usually recognizable by his bubble gum and baseball cap—we hope the guide's answer is a good one.

Fortunately, it will not be necessary to conduct any experiments to provide the tour guide with some answers. The necessary experiments were conducted by Galileo in the town of Pisa in northwestern Italy nearly 400 years ago. (Instead of arguing in a manner befitting the gentleman and scholar of those days, Galileo actually did something—he performed experiments. This, of course, was in very bad taste; and, despite the excellence of the building he used, his experiments did little more than earn him a reputation for thinking bad thoughts.)

Newton was born in the year that Galileo died. Not only did Newton fare better politically, he was able to develop the mathematics necessary to cope with Galileo's "bad thoughts" about the behavior of things in motion.

But to get back to the baseball! Let's assume the observation deck on the 60th floor is 784 feet above the street. The formula relating this distance in feet, S, to the time of flight of a free-falling object is

$$S = 16t^2,$$

in which t is measured in seconds. We can use this formula to see how long it will take for the baseball to reach the ground. We can also use it to illustrate the idea of a *derivative*.

When $S = 784'$, then $784 = 16t^2$, or $t^2 = 49$ and $t = 7$ seconds. In other words, from the time we release the baseball until it reaches the pavement 784' below, 7 seconds will elapse. From this we can compute the "average" velocity as follows:

$$
\begin{array}{ccc}
S & & t \\
\hline
0 & \ldots & 0 \\
784 & \ldots & 7
\end{array}
$$

$$\Delta S = 784 \qquad\qquad\qquad \Delta t = 7$$

$$\frac{\Delta S}{\Delta t} = \frac{784}{7} = 112 \text{ feet per second.}$$

This is the average velocity (or rate of change in distance) over the whole 7-second flight; but, if we are concerned about the damage the baseball might do when it hits the ground, this isn't a very useful "average." Certainly the ball started its flight at no velocity at all and gradually increased its speed as it fell. Hence, to have averaged 112 feet per second, its velocity must have been greater at the end of its flight to offset the slow start. Let's use the same formula to determine the average velocity during just the second half of its flight time. When $t = 3.5$ seconds, then $S = 16(3.5)^2 = 196$ feet.

$$
\begin{array}{ccc}
S & & t \\
\hline
196 & \ldots & 3.5 \\
784 & \ldots & 7.0
\end{array}
$$

$$\Delta S = 588 \qquad\qquad\qquad \Delta t = 3.5$$

$$\frac{\Delta S}{\Delta t} = \frac{588}{3.5} = 168 \text{ feet per second}$$

("average" velocity during the last 3.5 seconds).

This shows an increase as we suspected. Let us repeat this process for the last second of flight.

$$\begin{array}{cc} S & t \\ \hline 576 & \ldots 6 \\ 784 & \ldots 7 \end{array}$$

$\Delta S = 208$ $\qquad\qquad\qquad\qquad\qquad\qquad\qquad$ $\Delta t = 1$

$\dfrac{\Delta S}{\Delta t} = 208$ feet per second
$\qquad$ ("average" velocity during the last second).

And for the last tenth of a second:

$$\begin{array}{cc} S & t \\ \hline 761.76 & \ldots 6.9 \\ 784.00 & \ldots 7.0 \end{array}$$

$\Delta S = 22.24$ $\qquad\qquad\qquad\qquad\qquad\qquad$ $\Delta t = 0.1$

$\dfrac{\Delta S}{\Delta t} = \dfrac{22.24}{0.1} = 222.4$ feet per second
$\qquad$ ("average" velocity during
$\qquad\qquad$ the last tenth of a second).

2. Calculate the "average" velocity during the last 0.01 second of the baseball's fall.

$$\begin{array}{cc} S & t \\ \hline \underline{} & \ldots 6.99 \\ 784.0000 & \ldots 7.00 \end{array}$$

$\Delta S = \underline{}$ $\qquad\qquad\qquad\qquad\qquad$ $\Delta t = 0.01$

$\dfrac{\Delta S}{\Delta t} = \underline{}.$

Providing you have made no errors in arithmetic, this last approximation is the best estimate so far of the velocity of the baseball when it hits the pavement.[1] And, as you might have suspected, we have also been creeping up on one of the ideas that lie at the base of the calculus—the notion of a *limiting value*. In this case we have been pursuing the limiting value of $\Delta S/\Delta t$ as Δt got smaller and smaller. This limiting value of $\Delta S/\Delta t$ is called an *instantaneous rate of change* or the *derivative of S with respect to t*.

If we had taken $\Delta t = 0.0001$, $\Delta S/\Delta t$ would have come even closer to 224; in fact the smaller the value of Δt, the closer we would have come. We could in fact come as close as we wished to 224, because 224 is the limiting value of $\Delta S/\Delta t$ as Δt approaches zero. In the language of mathematics, this last sentence is written,

---

[1] 224 feet per second—a number your answer should be close to—is approximately 153 miles per hour.

$$\lim_{\Delta t \to 0} \left(\frac{\Delta S}{\Delta t} \right) = 224.$$

In the process of making Δt closer to zero, notice that ΔS also gets closer to zero. This causes many people to reason that if both the numerator and denominator are approaching zero then eventually they will equal zero. This, however, *is not the case*. And it's this fact that makes finding a limiting value a distinctly different kind of operation. To illustrate, consider the fraction

$$\frac{x^2 - 4}{x - 2}.$$

If we were to substitute 2 in place of x in this fraction, the result would be 0/0; but, if we evaluate

$$\lim_{x \to 2} \left(\frac{x^2 - 4}{x - 2} \right).$$

the result is 4. That is, the closer x gets to 2 (without actually equaling 2), the closer the value of this fraction gets to 4. That this is true is easier to comprehend if you recognize that $x^2 - 4/x - 2$ reduces to $(x + 2)(x - 2)/(x - 2)$ or simply $x + 2$.

In the problem concerning the baseball, our answers regarding the velocity at the time of impact got better and better as we made Δt closer to zero. But there is really no "best" answer to this problem. No matter how small we make the interval Δt we can always calculate a better answer by making it still smaller. By this process you can see that we never quite reach the *limit;* it remains a number to which all "good" answers are close.

We can now define in general terms the derivative for any two variables y and x, provided the value of y is determined by the value of x, as follows: *If $\Delta y/\Delta x$ has a limiting value as Δx approaches zero, this value is the derivative of y with respect to x, or the instantaneous rate of change of y with respect to x.* The process of finding the derivative is called *differentiation*, hence the term *differential calculus*.

If we have enough patience and either enough data or a formula which represents the data, we can compute the instantaneous rate of change for any value of the variable. For example:

In a recent study of the productivity of various-sized crews installing office partitioning, it was found that the following equation was approximately correct:

$$P = 54L - 3L^2,$$

where P is the number of panels installed in a week and L is the total labor dollars ($000) paid the crew during the week.

(The L^2 term with its minus sign was explained as representing the effect of men getting in each other's way and reducing crew efficiency as the number of men increased.)

At what rate does P increase as L increases? Just as before when it made a difference which value of t we chose, it now depends on which value of L we choose. Suppose we ask the question, "If we now have a $2,000 per week crew assigned, at what rate will P increase as we increase crew size?" We can perform calculations as follows:

$$L = 3 \qquad P = 54(3) - 3(9) = 135$$
$$L = 2 \qquad P = 54(2) - 3(4) = \;\;96$$

$$\text{rate of change at } L = 2 \text{ (1st approx.)}: \frac{39}{1} = 39$$

$$L = 2.1 \qquad P = 54(2.1) - 3(4.41) = 100.17$$
$$L = 2.0 \qquad P \qquad\qquad\qquad = \;\;96.00$$

$$\text{rate of change at } L = 2 \text{ (2nd approx.)}: \frac{4.17}{0.1} = 41.7$$

$$L = 2.01 \qquad P = 54(2.01) - 3(4.0401) = 96.4197$$
$$L = 2.00 \qquad P \qquad\qquad\qquad\quad = 96.0000$$

$$\text{rate of change at } L = 2 \text{ (3rd approx.)}: \frac{.4197}{.01} = 41.97.$$

As can be ascertained by continuing the computations of the above example further and further, the instantaneous rate of change of P at the point $L = 2$ is exactly 42. Whenever a digital computer is given a formula such as this one and asked to find the derivative at one or several points, it uses a process similar to the one shown in this example. In computer parlance, this is called *numerical differentiation.* Sometimes, actual data for several points on a curve are given instead of the formula for the curve. In such cases, numerical differentiation can be performed directly using special techniques designed for that purpose.

2.3 A GEOMETRIC INTERPRETATION

While numerical differentiation is convenient with a computer, it is extremely inconvenient if performed manually due to the excessive amount of computation involved. Mathematicians using the calculus avoid this by use of systematic and exact methods which we shall illustrate.

Let us begin by drawing a graph of the formula $P = 54 L - 3L^2$.

We do this by trying values of L and determining the corresponding values of P. Plotting the resulting points we find the curve to be as follows:

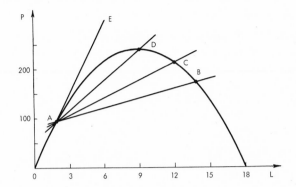

From the point A on the curve, we have drawn three straight lines, AB, AC, and AD, which intersect the curve at A and the points B, C, and D. Each of these straight lines are called *secants* to the curve, because they intersect the curve in *two* points. The secant AB cuts off the curve segment AB, secant AC cuts off a smaller curve segment AC, and the curve segment AD is smaller still. If more lines were drawn from the point A each of which cut off smaller and smaller curve segments, eventually a limiting line (represented by AE) would be reached which cuts off none of the curve. This limiting line touches the curve in just *one* point and is called *a tangent to the curve at point A.*

The slope of the three secants we have drawn can be determined by dividing the change in the variable P by the corresponding change in the variable L. For instance, the secant AB appears to cut the curve $P = 54L - 3L^2$ at the points $P = 96$, $L = 2$ and $P = 168$, $L = 14$. The change in P, therefore, is $168 - 96 = 72$ or $\Delta P = 72$, while $\Delta L = 14 - 2 = 12$. The slope of the secant AB, then, is $\Delta P/\Delta L = 72/12 = 6$. The slopes of all three secants are shown below:

Secant	Change in P	Change in L	Slope
AB . . .	$168 - 96 = 72$	$14 - 2 = 12$	$72/12 = 6$
AC . . .	$216 - 96 = 120$	$12 - 2 = 10$	$120/10 = 12$
AD . . .	$243 - 96 = 147$	$9 - 2 = 7$	$147/7 = 21$

If we continued such calculations for additional secants representing smaller and smaller changes in the variable L, the limiting value of this ratio will be just what we defined earlier as the derivative. Thus, the succession of secant lines gradually approaches the tangent line at point A, and the succession of slope calculations gradually approaches the value of the derivative at point A. The geometric interpretation of the derivative is therefore: *At a point on a curve, the value of the derivative at that point is equal to the slope of the tangent to the curve at that point.*

For the curve $P = 54L - 3L^2$, the tangent line at the point where $L = 2$ has a slope of 42. This is the limiting value of $\Delta P/\Delta L$ as ΔL gets smaller and smaller and the same value we approached in section 2.2.

 3. Using the following diagram, estimate the numerical value of the derivative at the point P, by sketching in the tangent line and estimating its slope:

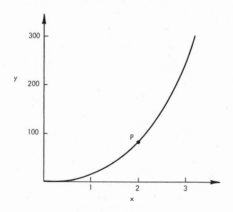

Value of derivative at point P: _____

The equivalence between the derivative and the slope of a tangent line is helpful in many ways. Some problems may require that we be able to construct a tangent to a curve at some point. The derivative enables us to do this. But there are many other more practical problems in which the slope of the tangent to a curve is important in addition to being able to construct graphs.

But before we consider such problems let us first find a more efficient way of finding derivatives. For this purpose the simple equation $y = x^2$ will serve well. How can we obtain a formula for the derivative of the curve $y = x^2$ so that at any value of x we can determine the slope of the tangent? The graph on the next page might help.

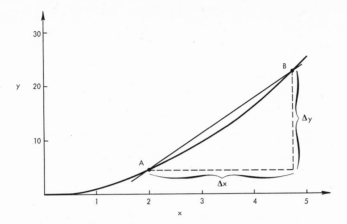

Let A be any point on the curve with co-ordinates (x,y). Let B be any other point through which we draw the secant AB. The co-ordinates of point B we can call $(x + \Delta x, y + \Delta y)$.

The slope of the secant AB is $\Delta y/\Delta x$. Since both points A and B are on the curve $y = x^2$, the co-ordinates of both points must satisfy the condition $y = x^2$. For point B, substituting $x + \Delta x$ and $y + \Delta y$ into the equation:

$$y + \Delta y = (x + \Delta x)^2,$$

which can be expanded and rewritten:

$$(1)\ y + \Delta y = x^2 + 2x\Delta x + (\Delta x)^2$$

and for point A, substituting x and y into the equation:

$$(2)\ y = x^2.$$

If we take the difference between the two equations, that is, subtract the equation (2) for point A from equation (1) for point B, we have:

$$(1)\ y + \Delta y = x^2 + 2x\Delta x + (\Delta x)^2$$
$$(2)\ y \qquad\quad = x^2$$
$$\overline{ \Delta y = \qquad 2x\Delta x + (\Delta x)^2.}$$

Dividing both sides by Δx gives us:

$$\frac{\Delta y}{\Delta x} = 2x + \Delta x.$$

This is the formula for the slope of the secant AB, or, for that matter, any other secant we might draw. For instance, if we desire the slope of the secant between points $x = 2$ and 5 respectively, then:

$$x = 2, \Delta x = 3$$

$$\frac{\Delta y}{\Delta x} = 2x + \Delta x = 4 + 3 = 7.$$

But to find the derivative or slope of the *tangent* at point A, we need the *limit* of the slope as Δx approaches zero (i.e., as point B gets closer and closer to point A.) Looking at the formula we just derived for the slope of the secant, we find this limit as follows:

$$\lim_{\Delta x \to 0} \left(\frac{\Delta y}{\Delta x} \right) = \lim_{\Delta x \to 0} (2x + \Delta x) = 2x.$$

In this case, since there is no division involved, it is not difficult to see that $2x$ is the limiting value. It is also the formula for the derivative.

In practice, the symbol dy/dx (pronounced "*dy* by *dx*") is used to represent the derivative. In this case $dy/dx = 2x$ so the slope of the tangent, then at the point $x = 2$, is

$$\frac{dy}{dx} = 2x = 4.$$

This same formula could be used to find the slope of the tangent to the curve $y = x^2$ at any value of x.

4. Find a formula for the derivative of $y = 6x^2 - 5x$ by finishing the derivative begun below:

$$y + \Delta y = 6(x + \Delta x)^2 - 5(x + \Delta x)$$
$$y + \Delta y = 6x^2 + 12x\Delta x + 6(\Delta x)^2 - 5x - 5\Delta x$$
$$\underline{y \qquad\quad = 6x^2 \qquad\qquad\qquad - 5x}$$
$$\Delta y =$$
$$\frac{\Delta y}{\Delta x} =$$
$$\lim_{\Delta x \to 0} \left(\frac{\Delta y}{\Delta x} \right) = \frac{dy}{dx} = \underline{\qquad\qquad}.$$

5. Using the method of the previous exercise, find a formula for the derivative of $y = 2x^2 + 3$

$$\frac{dy}{dx} = \underline{\qquad\qquad}$$

2.4   RULES FOR FINDING DERIVATIVES

The rules for finding derivatives of many algebraic expressions have been worked out in a manner similar to the way we found the derivative of y with respect to x in the equation $y = x^2$. Rather than continuing to find derivatives by this "delta" method, we shall state the general rule for finding the derivative for any power function as follows:

$$\text{if} \qquad y = x^n$$

$$\text{then} \qquad \frac{dy}{dx} = nx^{n-1}.$$

This formula is sometimes written as

$$\frac{d}{dx}(x^n) = nx^{n-1}$$

to avoid confusion regarding the original expression to which the formula applies. The formula states that the derivative is equal to the exponent of the independent variable multiplied by the variable itself with its exponent reduced by 1. The rule holds for any value of n whether positive, negative, an integer, fraction, etc. The following examples illustrate application of the formula:

(1) $y = x^4$ $\qquad$ (2) $y = x^{-7}$ $\qquad$ (3) $y = x^1$

$\quad \frac{dy}{dx} = 4x^3$ $\qquad\quad \frac{dy}{dx} = -7x^{-8}$ $\qquad\quad \frac{dy}{dx} = 1x^0 = 1$

If x had had a coefficient, say "a," the rule is still the same:

$$y = ax^n$$

$$\frac{dy}{dx} = anx^{n-1}.$$

For example:

$$y = 3x^2$$

$$\frac{dy}{dx} = 3(2x^1) = 6x.$$

We can show the effect of any coefficient "a" by using the same method we used earlier to find the derivative of $y = x^2$ as follows:

$$y = ax^2$$
$$(y + \Delta y) = a(x + \Delta x)^2 \qquad \text{(subtract)}$$
$$y \qquad\qquad = ax^2$$
$$\overline{\qquad\qquad\qquad\qquad\qquad\qquad}$$
$$\Delta y = a[x^2 + 2x(\Delta x) + (\Delta x)^2] - ax^2$$
$$\Delta y = 2ax(\Delta x) + a(\Delta x)^2.$$

Dividing through by Δx:

$$\frac{\Delta y}{\Delta x} = 2ax + a\Delta x.$$

Letting Δx approach zero:

$$\lim_{\Delta x \to 0} \left(\frac{\Delta y}{\Delta x}\right) = \frac{dy}{dx} = 2ax.$$

The net result is that the derivative is "a" times as large. Thus, the derivative of $y = 5x^3$ is

$$\frac{dy}{dx} = 5(3x^2) = 15x^2.$$

The derivative of $y = 2x$ is:

$$\frac{dy}{dx} = 2x^0 = 2.$$

And the derivative of $y = 4$ (i.e., $y = 4x^0$) is:

$$\frac{dy}{dx} = (4)(0)x^{-1} = 0.$$

In general, then, we see that the fundamental rule for finding the derivative of a power of x holds for a constant as well, because a constant can be considered to be multiplied by x to the zeroth power. A simpler way to write this rule is:

$$y = a$$
$$\frac{dy}{dx} = 0.$$

6. Use the rule for differentiating powers to find derivatives of the following:

$$y = 2x^5 \qquad \frac{dy}{dx} = \underline{\hspace{3cm}}$$

$$R = 3S^{-2} \qquad \frac{dR}{dS} = \underline{\hspace{3cm}}$$

$$y = ax^b \qquad \frac{dy}{dx} = \underline{\hspace{3cm}}$$

$$y = 2x^{-1/2} \qquad \frac{dy}{dx} = \underline{\hspace{3cm}}$$

Another useful rule is that *the derivative of the sum of a number of terms is equal to the sum of the derivatives of the individual terms.* To illustrate, let y equal the sum of the terms $2x^3$, $-3x^2$, $-x$, and 5. In other words, $y = 2x^3 - 3x^2 - x + 5$. Following this rule, then, the derivative of this sum is

$$\frac{dy}{dx} = 6x^2 - 6x - 1.$$

Without attempting to prove the above rule, perhaps you can imagine a limit being approached by each of the original terms individually as Δx approaches zero. It should not be surprising, then, to find that this limit of their sum is just the sum of these individual limiting values as the rule states.

7. Find the derivative of $y = 3x^5 - 4x^3 + 2x - 7$

$$\frac{dy}{dx} = \underline{\hspace{3cm}}$$

8. Find the slope of the tangent to the curve in the exercise above at the point $x = 1$.

Slope = \underline{\hspace{3cm}}

The knowledge that the derivative of $y = bx$ is the constant b, i.e., $(dy/dx) = b$, helps us now to understand better why, in the equation of the straight line $(y = a + bx)$, b was always the slope of the line. The tangent to a line, of course, is just the line itself, and therefore its slope must remain constant.

To show the application of the rule for differentiating power functions, let us rework the example cited earlier:

In a recent study of the productivity of various sized crews in building construction, it was found that the following equation was approximately correct:

$$P = 54L - 3L^2$$

where P is the number of panels installed in a week and L is the total labor dollars ($\$000$) paid the crew during the week. If we now have a $\$2,000$ per week crew assigned, at what rate will P increase as we increase crew size? Applying the formula for differentiating powers:

$$\frac{dP}{dL} = 54 - 6L$$

substituting $L = 2$ into this formula:

$$\frac{dP}{dL} \text{ (at } L = 2) = 54 - 6(2) = 42.$$

This was the value which was approached as a limit in our previous calculations, in which we let ΔL take on successively smaller values.

Now that we have a *formula* for the derivative of P with respect to L, instead of just a numerical answer for one value of L, other observations can be made. The formula:

$$\frac{dP}{dL} = 54 - 6L,$$

shows that the derivative gets smaller as L gets larger, because of the minus sign. In other words, the bigger the size of the crew (L) to start with, the smaller the increase in productivity which can be obtained for a unit increase in crew size. For example, when $L =$ $2 thousand, P changes at the rate of 42 panels per thousand dollars, whereas at $L =$ $7 thousand, P changes at only 12 ($= 54 - 6 \cdot 7$) panels per thousand dollars. This is an illustration of the economic principle called the law of diminishing returns, in which each additional unit of input yields progressively fewer additional units of output.

9. In this example, at what crew size does the expenditure of additional dollars for increased crew yield *no* increase in panel output?

$$L = \text{_____}$$

Actually, the determination of instantaneous rates of change is not especially useful in itself and would not justify the application of the calculus on that basis alone. There *are* common problems, however, which cannot be solved practically, if at all, without deriving a formula for the instantaneous rate of change. Usually, it is the formula itself which is combined mathematically with other formulas, so that an over-all answer to a business problem is derived without computing any numerical values of the instantaneous rates of change of the variables in the problem.

2.5 MAXIMUM AND MINIMUM PROBLEMS

Another use we can make of the derivative relates to maximum and minimum points on a graph of y versus x, especially in finding the values of x at which these extreme values of y occur. Notice

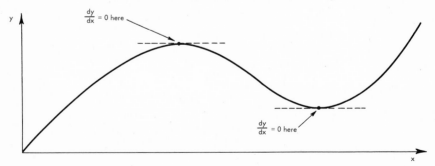

that at the maximum and minimum points the tangent is horizontal, that is, its slope dy/dx is 0, because at such points the instantaneous rate of change of y with respect to x is zero. All the tangents at points just to the left of a maximum point have positive or upward slopes; all the tangents at points just to the right of the maximum point have negative or downward slopes. Now if the slope of the tangent is positive on one side and negative on the other, and it is changing continuously, then it *must* be exactly zero at some intermediate point.

To illustrate the power of this basic concept, consider its application in the following profit-maximization problem:

Suppose that the unit sales volume V of a certain model appliance depends on the offering price P, according to the following equation:

$$V = 80,000 - 10,000P.$$

While this linear demand function can ordinarily represent an actual case only in a limited range of price, let us suppose it to be acceptable for this example.

Suppose in addition that the total cost C involved in producing V units is given by the following equation:

$$C = 65,000 + 2V.$$

In other words, the fixed costs allocated to this model appliance are $65,000, and the unit variable cost is $2.00.

Given this information, what price will yield the greatest gross margin? This problem is easily solved with the differential calculus, as follows:

$$\text{Total Margin} = M = \text{Total Revenue minus Total Cost}$$
$$M = (\text{Price})(\text{Volume}) - (\text{Cost})$$
$$M = PV - C$$
$$PV = P\,(80,000 - 10,000P)$$
$$= 80,000P - 10,000P^2$$
$$C = 65,000 + 2V$$
$$= 65,000 + 2(80,000 - 10,000P)$$
$$= 225,000 - 20,000P$$
$$M = (80,000P - 10,000P^2) - (225,000 - 20,000P)$$
$$= 100,000P - 10,000P^2 - 225,000.$$

Differentiating M with respect to P:

$$\frac{dM}{dP} = 100,000\,(1)\,P^0 - 10,000\,(2)\,P^1 - 225,000\,(0)P^{-1}$$
$$= 100,000 - 20,000P.$$

This last formula is an expression giving the rate of change of margin with price. Now the value of P which yields the maximum margin is exactly the point at which the margin is *not changing*—at the point where the margin has "just barely stopped increasing" and is "getting ready to begin decreasing." This is the point at which the slope of the curve is *zero*. To find this point, we simply set the formula for the slope of the tangent (the formula above for the derivative) equal to zero, and solve the algebraic equation that results. In this case,

$$\frac{dM}{dP} = 100,000 - 20,000P = 0$$
$$20,000P = 100,000$$
$$P = 5.$$

According to this, gross margin should be largest when the selling price is set at $5.00. Although it is a crude way to do it, suppose we verify this by calculating margin for this price and for prices just a little higher and a little lower:

	$ 4.90	$ 5.00	$ 5.10
Price:			
Volume = 80,000 − 10,000P:	31,000	30,000	29,000
Revenue = (Price)(Volume)	151,900	150,000	147,900
Cost = 65,000 + 2V:	127,000	125,000	123,000
Margin = Revenue − Cost:	$ 24,900	$ 25,000	$ 24,900

As predicted, the choice of $5.00 yields the maximum margin.

At this point, most people feel fairly comfortable with the answer $P = \$5.00$, probably because it is a concrete numerical value which looks like a reasonable price to charge for a small appliance. However, appearances can be deceptive, especially when the really important things are hidden from view. In the process of working out this answer *arithmetically*, i.e., doing all the arithmetic operations we could as we went along, we obscured the true nature of the problem and covered up the assumptions which are built into it. It is for this reason that mathematicians often *prefer* to work out problems using symbols other than numerals, saving until the very last the actual substitution of constants to get the final answer. Let's see what would happen if we used this approach on this problem.

Suppose the unit sales volume V of a certain model appliance depends on the offering price P, according to the following equation:

$$V = a - bP.$$

The constants "a" and "b" can be interpreted from the equation directly.

If the price P is set equal to zero, then $V = a$, so that "a" is the number of appliances that can be "given away" at zero price. If we set $V = 0$, we can solve for P to get $P = a/b$, so that the ratio a/b is the price at which we sell no appliances at all. In other words, the last customer says "t'aint wuth it" at this price. (In the actual problem we started with, the zero-price volume is 80,000 units, and the no-volume price is 80,000/10,000 or $8.00.)

Suppose in addition that the total cost C involved in producing V units is given by the following equation:

$$C = f + gV.$$

The constants "f" and "g" can be interpreted directly: the fixed costs are equal to f and the variable cost per unit is g. (In the actual problem we started with, the fixed costs were $65,000 and the unit variable cost was $2.00.)

As the first step toward finding a *formula* for the optimum price, we express margin M in terms of price P:

$$\text{Total Margin} = \text{Total Revenue minus Total Cost}$$
$$M = (\text{Price})(\text{Volume}) - (\text{Cost})$$
$$M = PV - C$$

$$PV = P(a - bP)$$
$$= aP - bP^2$$

$$C = f + gV$$
$$= f + g(a - bP)$$
$$= f + ga - gbP$$
$$M = aP - bP^2 - f - ga + gbP$$

$$\frac{dM}{dP} = a - 2bP + gb.$$

Setting the derivative equal to zero to find the value of P at which M is a maximum:

$$a - 2bP + gb = 0$$
$$2bP = a + gb$$
$$P = \frac{1}{2}\left(\frac{a}{b} + g\right).$$

This is the desired formula for the optimum price. The numerical value for the example can be found by substituting $a = 80,000$, $b = 10,000$, $f = 65,000$, and $g = 2$:

$$P = \frac{1}{2}\left(\frac{80,000}{10,000} + 2\right) = 5,$$

which is the same answer as before.

But what *general* conclusions about this problem can be drawn from the formula for optimum price? For purposes of illustration, let us draw several conclusions based on the premises we have used.

Premises: $V = a \quad - bP$
$$C = f \quad + gV$$
$$M = PV - C$$

Conclusions:

1. $P_{(for\ max\ M)} = \dfrac{1}{2}\left(\dfrac{a}{b} + g\right).$

2. Since the unit variable cost g will always be greater than zero, the formula shows that the optimum price will *always* be greater than $a/2b$. (In the example with $a = 80{,}000$ and $b = 10{,}000$, the optimum price is always greater than $4.00, regardless of what the variable cost is.)

3. Since the fixed cost f does not appear in the formula for optimum price, the decision as to what price to set for maximum margin is *independent* of the level of fixed costs. (In the example, if fixed costs were different from $65,000, the actual margin obtained at the optimum price would be different, but the optimum price of $5.00 would still be exactly the same.)

4. Since the optimum price increases when a/b increases, any action in such a marketplace which increases a/b should be accompanied by a corresponding increase in price, if margin is to be maximized. Since a/b is the price which is so high that no one buys, such actions as advertising and sales promotion would tend to change this no-volume price. (In this example, if additional sales promotion expenditures result in an increase in the $8.00 no-volume price, the actual offering price should be raised to maintain optimum margin.)

5. Since the optimum price decreases when the unit variable cost g decreases, any reduction in unit cost should be reflected in a corresponding price reduction. (In the example, a reduction of unit variable cost from $2.00 to $1.80, for instance, should be accompanied by a reduction of price from $5.00 to $4.90, if margin is to be maximized.)

The above is *not* an all-purpose pricing model. It is an analysis of the characteristics of a market in which the relationships between price and demand is *linear* and to which is offered a product whose cost is *linearly* related to unit volume. Most businesses, of course, are much more complicated than this, and require correspondingly more complicated analyses. The demand curves and the cost equations will need to be derived on the basis of experience, using methods such as those described in Chapter 5.

Before returning to our discussion of calculus itself, there are three important observations on the use of mathematics in business which are well illustrated by the last example. First, a mathematical analysis is no better than the assumptions which underlie it. In the above example the conclusions are logically implied by the *premises*. The conclusions, however, are valid only if the premises accurately describe a particular business situation. Therefore, a purely numerical analysis in which the assumptions and their implications are all "washed out" by the arithmetic should be used with care in complicated situations, because the numerical answer provides no basis for *testing* the assumptions. Secondly, the most innocent-looking premises can lead logically to some very startling conclusions, so that a method of analysis which permits drawing an assortment of conclusions is usually to be preferred over one which just yields "the answer." Third, mathematics most frequently comes under attack when its application to business problems results in unreasonable conclusions. Frequently the source of difficulty stems not from inaccuracies in mathematical manipulation, but from the premises upon which the analysis is based. In this regard the business manager is often best qualified and should, therefore, monitor the assumptions which enter the mathematician's analysis.

2.6 INTEGRAL CALCULUS

The way we "undo" the result of addition is to use subtraction; the way we "undo" multiplication is to use division. In a similar way, the *integral calculus* "undoes" what is accomplished by the differential calculus. In the differential calculus we started with an equation or formula and, by applying certain rules, we found its derivative. In the integral calculus the derivative is known and it is the equation that must be determined. For example, if we have a formula like $dy/dx = 2x^2 + x + 3$, a little thought as to how such derivatives are formed might lead us to deduce the following rule for "undoing" differentiation: *raise the power of each term by one and divide by the new exponent*. Applying this rule to the formula for dy/dx yields:

$$y = \frac{2}{3}x^3 + \frac{1}{2}x^2 + 3x + c.$$

(The c tacked on the end represents a constant and serves as a reminder that no matter what value we assign to c, the derivative of y is unchanged. The reason, of course, is that the derivative of a constant is zero. Since we get no clues as to the specific value of the constant term from dy/dx, we make provisions for the constant by adding the c.)

Here are some exercises to practice on, a few of which are already worked out for you.

 10. (Use the symbol c to stand for an arbitrary constant.)

$$\frac{dy}{dx} = 1 \qquad\qquad y = \underline{\quad\quad x + c \quad\quad}$$

$$\frac{dR}{dt} = 2t + a \qquad\qquad R = \underline{\quad t^2 + at + c \quad}$$

$$\frac{dy}{dx} = 6x^2 + 1 \qquad\qquad y = \underline{\qquad\qquad\qquad}$$

$$\frac{dy}{dx} = 3 - \frac{1}{2}x \qquad\qquad y = \underline{\qquad\qquad\qquad}$$

$$\frac{dL}{dm} = a + b \qquad\qquad L = \underline{\qquad\qquad\qquad}$$

The operation you performed in the exercise above is called *integration,* and the rule you used is one of many rules for integrating. This particular rule was not difficult to deduce. Given $dy/dx = ax^n$, we found

$$y = \frac{ax^{n+1}}{n+1} + c.$$

As it turns out, not all of the rules for integrating are this simple. Some expressions, in fact, cannot be integrated at all. Another problem with integration is that we are left with an unknown constant whose value is impossible to determine without additional information. These difficulties make the integral calculus a good deal more complex than the differential calculus. Integration is nonetheless a very useful tool in many practical problems.

To illustrate one such problem, let us consider an example in which something is known about rates of change (the derivative) and the problem is one of determining the relationships among the variables. This particular example involves an economic theory in which the relationship between the variables national income and national debt is sought.[1]

Suppose we assume that national income I increases at a constant rate

---

[1] This theory is known as the Domar Debt Model, after E. Domar, the economist who suggested it in the *American Economic Review* (1944).

with time, say a dollars per year. Assume that the rate of increase of the national debt D is proportional to the level of national income. In equation form, these two conditions are:

$$\frac{dI}{dt} = a \qquad \text{and} \qquad \frac{dD}{dt} = bI,$$

where t stands for time and b is a proportionality constant. Our job is to find equations for income I and for debt D in terms of time and constants. This is a differential equation problem and one uses integral calculus to solve it.

What is the derivative with respect to t of the expression "at"? The answer, of course, is a, as we have already seen. But for any constant c, the derivative of the expression $at + c$ is *also* a. No matter what value c has, even zero, the derivative is the same. Remembering this, starting with:

$$\frac{dI}{dt} = a$$

leads us to immediately conclude:

$$I = at + c.$$

We have just found the general solution of the first of the two original equations. Suppose we knew that the national income had the value I_0 in a base year for which we let $t = 0$. We then use this initial condition to find c:

$$I_0 = a(0) + c$$

or

$$c = I_0.$$

Hence, $I = at + I_0$ is the equation expressing income in terms of time t and known constants.

Turning now to the second equation, we substitute the derived formula for I into the right side of it to get:

$$\frac{dD}{dt} = bI = b(at + I_0) = abt + bI_0.$$

To get a formula for D, we need to find what expression, when differentiated, yields $abt + bI_0$. The answer is:

$$D = \frac{1}{2}(ab)t^2 + (bI_0)\, t + k,$$

where k is some new constant. As before, suppose we let D_0 stand for the national debt in the base year when $t = 0$:

$$D_0 = \frac{1}{2}(ab)(0)^2 + (bI_0)(0) + k$$

or

$$k = D_0.$$

The two equations we were seeking are then as follows:

$$I = (a)t + (I_0)$$

$$D = \left(\frac{1}{2} ab\right)t^2 + (bI_0)t + (D_0).$$

To give a better idea about these equations and how they relate to the original differential equations with which the example started, imagine that in the year 1961 the national income of a certain country were 100 billion, and its national debt were 50 billion. Imagine that the income were increasing at the constant rate of 10 billion per year, and that the national debt is increasing at an annual rate equal to 5 per cent of the national income. In terms of the constants of the model:

$$t = 0 \qquad \text{for base year 1961}$$
$$I_0 = 100, \qquad\qquad D_0 = 50$$
$$a = 10, \qquad\qquad b = .05$$

The differential equations become:

$$\frac{dI}{dt} = a = 10 \text{ and } \frac{dD}{dt} = bI = .05I.$$

The solutions to these equations are:

$$I = a(t) + (I_0) = 10t + 100$$

$$D = \left(\frac{1}{2}ab\right)t^2 + (bI_0)t + (D_0)$$

$$= 0.25t^2 + 5t + 50.$$

In the year 1965 then, the national income will be 140 billion and the debt 74 billion, found by putting $t = 4$ into the equations for I and D.

As a postscript to this example, Domar was primarily interested in the ratio of national debt to national income, and what happens to this ratio as time marches on. In this theory, it can be easily shown mathematically that this ratio approaches infinity. In other words, with these assumptions about how income and debt change, the debt would eventually grow beyond all bounds. Perhaps the unpleasantness of this prospect is what has encouraged other models to be made—models which are based on a different set of assumptions which are more realistic and commensurately more complicated mathematically.

No brief description of the calculus should omit mention of the important mathematical expression $y = ae^{bx}$ which arises in so many practical problems involving growth phenomena. As described in Chapter 5, this is the exponential trend which was found applicable in situations ranging from the growth of bacteria to the accumulation of money at compound interest. With the basic ideas of calculus in mind, we now take a look at the way this equation arises in certain kinds of situations.

Hardly anyone would disagree with the statement "the interest earned is proportional to the amount of principal on deposit." A biologist knows that a colony of bacteria grows at a rate proportional to its size. Growth processes in which the variable doing the growing is changing at a rate proportional to the variable itself are characterized by the same kind of differential equation. Letting y be the variable which is changing over time x, the equation can be written:

$$\frac{dy}{dx} = by.$$

In other words, the rate of change in y at any instant is some constant b times the value of y at that same instant.

How can this differential equation be solved? We desire an equation for y in terms of x, but y appears on the right side of the differential equation and x appears not at all. Actually, if we forget about the constant b for a moment, this equation is simply saying that some formula for y in terms of x is to be found which is the same as its own derivative. What formula can this be? Certainly not any of the powers like x^2, x^3, etc., because their derivatives always have exponents decreased by one.

Mathematicians searched for this particular formula, and finally discovered that the number 2.71828182845904523536 · · · (which they thankfully agreed to call "e") had the amazing property that when it was raised to a variable power, the result was an expression which was equal to its own derivative. Furthermore, it was the *only* expression with this property. So, another formula from differential calculus is:

$$\frac{d}{dx}(e^x) = e^x,$$

because e is *defined* that way. The number e is generally referred to as the base of natural logarithms; it got to be that because it is an especially good number to raise to various powers. Natural logarithms are commonly used in higher mathematics (instead of the "common" base 10 logarithms) because they are so convenient, so *natural*.

As it happens, the complete solution to our original differential equation

$$\frac{dy}{dx} = by$$

is the exponential trend equation $y = ae^{bx}$. The constant "a" arises because the differential equation holds no matter what constant is included as a multiplier of e^{bx}.

As so often happens in mathematics, it is the simple ideas, the simple equations, which are the most fundamental and the most valuable to the user of mathematical methods. About the *simplest* of all differential equations, as any mathematician will testify, are the following (in which a and b are constant):

$$(1)\ \frac{dy}{dx} = ax^b \qquad (2)\ \frac{dy}{dx} = by.$$

All of the types of algebraic equations considered in Chapter 5 are derived from these two differential equations! From (1) comes the hyperbola if $b = -2$, the linear equation if $b = 0$, and the power function for any positive value of b. From (2) comes the exponential equation as we have seen above.

Practice Problems

PROBLEM I

In a study of the total cost of sampling information for accounting purposes, it was found that the equation,

$$C = 0.04n + \frac{5.12}{\sqrt{n}},$$

described the total cost C, when n was the number of items in the sample. The 0.04 was the unit cost of sampling an item, and the 5.12 was the cost of a unit error in estimation.

Using this equation, what is the number of items to be sampled which minimizes the total cost C?

(Hint: rewrite $5.12/\sqrt{n}$ as $5.12n^{-1/2}$.)

PROBLEM II

On the basis of a pricing experiment in test markets on the sales of a newly designed kitchen clock-timer, the following data on estimated sales demand was obtained:

Offering Price	Est. Weekly Sales Volume (Units)
$5.79	3,500
6.69	2,600
7.98	2,250
9.98	900

Cost Accounting has estimated the variable costs on these units to be $3.05 each, and weekly fixed costs on the new clock-timer line to be about $7,000.

On the basis of this information, at what price should the new clock-timer be offered to produce maximum margin? (Note: Fit a *straight line* to the data to determine the price volume relationship.)

CHAPTER 7

Matrices and Their Uses

1. Introduction

1.1 WHAT T. C. MITS MISSED

And so you know that
Algebra is a sort of
Generalized Arithmetic
by which more difficult problems
may be solved.
That Geometry is
not only the study of
various figures in
two and three dimensions,
but is also
a sample science,
the entire structure of which
is built up from
a few basic postulates—
and is therefore a "model"
for any system of thought.
That Analytic Geometry is
a combination of
Algebra and Geometry which
has proved extremely useful.
And that Calculus is
a powerful instrument for
the study of
our DYNAMIC world.

You know also that
Mathematics is useful not only
as a technique,

but also as a sample of
a method of thinking:
it is clear,
precise,
brief,
many-sided.
That a THOUGHTFUL study of
even a little Mathematics
can throw much light on
many controversies,
even with very little use of
mathematical technique. . . .

Perhaps you may say:
"What more can we ask?"

But the fact is that
all the branches of Mathematics
mentioned . . .
had been discovered
by the time of Newton,
who lived from 1642 to 1727.
And it was he who
invented the Calculus.
Analytic Geometry dates from Descartes,
about 1637.
Euclid goes back to
about 300 B.C.
And a good deal of the Algebra
which is studied in
high school and college
is spread out
from as far back as
about 3000 B.C. to
the time of Newton.
Thus,
the knowledge of Mathematics
of the average college graduate
stops with what was known
about 300 years ago!
And yet
more Mathematics has been invented
in the last 100 years
than in all the previous centuries

taken together!
If the same were true about
the study of Physics,
the average college graduate would
never even have heard of
an airplane or
an automobile or
a radio,
etc., etc.
Such a situation in Physics
would never have been tolerated.

Why then is it tolerated in
Mathematics?
Perhaps MODERN Mathematics is
so difficult that
it can be understood only by
a few rare souls?
Not at all!
Of course it took
a few VERY RARE souls indeed
to CREATE it,
But these new results are
no harder to understand than
any of the older Mathematics.

Perhaps it is just inertia
on the part of some educators?
And T.C.,
not being aware of
what he is missing,
does not clamor for it!

We feel that he can get even more of
an intelligent, general outlook on
life
from the MODERN ideas than
from the older ones![1]

1.2 THE ROLE OF "MODERN" MATHEMATICS

The first six chapters of this course in Basic Mathematics have

---

[1] H. G. and L. R. Lieber, *The Education of T. C. Mits* (Rev. ed.; New York: W. W. Norton & Co., Inc., 1942, 1944), pp. 43-47. Published in England by George Allen & Unwin Ltd.

been aimed at what the Liebers (over 20 years ago!) labeled for T. C. Mits as "old" mathematics. The last two chapters, this one on Matrices and Chapter 8 on the Algebra of Sets, can properly be called "modern" mathematics, having been in existence for only a hundred years or so. But as history goes, this is a relatively short time—it is only natural to expect that the mathematics which man invented *first* were those kinds he needed *most*. This is so true that even today in the 1960's, 90 per cent of all the problems are attacked and solved with the old standard methods. Why then study the newer mathematics if it can be used to directly address only a few problems?

The reason is twofold: first, the newer branches of mathematics have arisen partly in response to newly recognized *kinds* of problems. Thus, many of the problems that come up in our modern industrial world simply cannot be solved except by the newer techniques. Secondly, much of modern mathematics came into being because its inventors were mathematicians trying to extend the frontiers of the *old* mathematics. In trying to make the older methods more complete or more satisfying, they stumbled (not accidentally, as a rule) onto some very powerful ideas which seemed to pull together and unify several different branches of mathematics.

One such idea is the concept of a *set,* which is so simple it appears at first glance to be ridiculous. Yet this one notion and the theory which is founded upon it has, from about 1875 onwards, revolutionized not only a large part of mathematical knowledge, but even more important for us, has also begun to revolutionize the method of *teaching* the"old" mathematics. Set Theory does have some important *direct* applications in its own right, as we will see in Chapter 8, but the best reason for learning about it now is the indirect value to a person who is exploring for the first time in such areas as probability theory, relations and functions, advanced algebra, mathematical programing, symbolic logic, and so on.

Another such fundamental idea is that of a *matrix.* Just as with sets, the basic ideas of matrix theory are extremely simple, because they relate so closely to the way we think and the way we calculate with numbers. In fact, the ideas are so self-evident that we can wonder why we must go to so much trouble—"much ado about nothing" as it were. But to underrate the power of these ideas would be a grave mistake. Their very simplicity is the source of their power throughout mathematics, because they can be applied so widely.

The student of formal logic would recognize this as just one more illustration of the difference between the *intension* and the *extension* of a concept. An idea such as "means of transportation" has little intension but much extension, since it says very little about any one thing to which it applies, but it applies to a very great number of things. A concept such as "Boat-tailed Auburn Speedster" has great intension but very small extension, since it conveys a world of meaning to a classic car enthusiast, but the number of specific instances in which the concept applies is extremely limited. The rule in logic is that what you gain in intension you must sacrifice in extension, and vice versa, i.e., with a single idea or concept you can convey a little bit of information about many things, or much information about a few things.

The notion of a matrix is an instance of a concept with great extension, for it applies all across mathematics: in linear algebra, in regression theory, in mathematical programing, in statistical mechanics, in queuing theory, in Markov processes, in game theory, and so on and on. But the concept has small intension: it says just a little about a set of ordinary numbers, namely that they are arranged in a particular way, in rows and columns, much as traffic lights in a city are arranged at the intersection of the streets and avenues. Any one of the numbers in the arrangement, at the intersection of one row and one column, is just an ordinary number. When speaking about just one row or one column of numbers, we call the string of numbers a *vector*. Since a *matrix* is just a collection of numbers arranged into rows and columns, we could say, correctly, that a matrix with just *one* row is a vector (a *row* vector) and a matrix with just one column is also a vector (a *column* vector). Similarly, a matrix with just one row and one column, or a row vector with just one column, or a column vector with just one row, is equivalent to a single number.

Confused already? Suppose we take these (simple?) ideas one at a time, and as we go along, see how they are used in various familiar ways, such as adding and multiplying differing collections of numbers together. At the conclusion of this chapter—as a means of pointing out the extraordinary range of ways in which matrices may find application—we shall discuss a couple of familiar problems to which the application of the matrix is both direct and also readily observable.

2.   Vector and Matrix Operations

2.1   VECTORS

A *vector* is a string of numbers in single file. If the numbers are strung out vertically, the resulting vector is called a *column vector*. If strung out horizontally, the result is called a *row vector*. Here are some samples of each:

Column Vectors

$$\begin{pmatrix} 2 \\ 1 \end{pmatrix} \qquad \begin{pmatrix} 5 \\ 9 \end{pmatrix} \qquad \begin{pmatrix} 1 \\ 0 \\ 1 \end{pmatrix} \qquad \begin{pmatrix} 3 \\ 4 \\ -1 \\ 2 \end{pmatrix}$$

Row Vectors

$$(1, 2), \qquad (3, -2), \qquad (1, 0, -1, 1), \qquad (10, 20)$$

Individual numbers contained within a vector are called *components,* and an important characteristic of a vector is the number of components that it contains. The first two vectors above have two components each; these are two-component column vectors. The last two vectors illustrated are, respectively, a four-component row vector and a two-component row vector.

Two row vectors, or two column vectors, are *equal* if the *corresponding* components of each are equal. To illustrate, for the vectors

$$a = (5, 7), \qquad b = \begin{pmatrix} 5 \\ 7 \end{pmatrix}, \qquad c = (5, 7), \qquad d = (7, 5)$$

we find that

$$a = c \text{ but } a \neq b \text{ and } c \neq d.$$

The *sum* of two vectors is defined as the result obtained from componentwise addition. For example:

$$\begin{pmatrix} 4 \\ -1 \\ 2 \end{pmatrix} + \begin{pmatrix} 2 \\ 3 \\ -4 \end{pmatrix} = \begin{pmatrix} 6 \\ 2 \\ -2 \end{pmatrix}$$

and

$$(4, -9, 12) + (5, 11, -14) = (9, 2, -2).$$

Observe that we do not allow the addition of two vectors unless they are both row or both column vectors, having the same number of components.

Having defined the operation of adding two vectors, we can easily guess how one would add three or more vectors.

$$\begin{pmatrix} 1 \\ 1 \\ 1 \end{pmatrix} + \begin{pmatrix} 0 \\ 1 \\ 1 \end{pmatrix} + \begin{pmatrix} 0 \\ 0 \\ 1 \end{pmatrix} = \begin{pmatrix} 1 \\ 2 \\ 3 \end{pmatrix}$$

and

$$(1, 1, 1) + (0, 1, 1,) , (0, 0, 1) = (1, 2, 3).$$

In general, any number of vectors (row or column) may be added if they each contain the same number of components. The sum is a new vector whose first component is the sum of the first components of the original vectors, whose second component is the sum of the second components, and so on.

Multiplication of a vector by a number is performed by multiplying each component of the vector by the number. For example, if we let a represent a constant by which the column vector (represented by x) is to be multiplied, the result for a three-component case would be:

$$ax = a \begin{pmatrix} x_1 \\ x_2 \\ x_3 \end{pmatrix} = \begin{pmatrix} ax_1 \\ ax_2 \\ ax_3 \end{pmatrix}$$

and if x had been a three-component row vector:

$$ax = a(x_1, x_2, x_3) = (ax_1, ax_2, ax_3).$$

Illustrating this numerically, we have

$$3 \cdot \begin{pmatrix} 2 \\ 1 \\ 6 \end{pmatrix} = \begin{pmatrix} 6 \\ 3 \\ 18 \end{pmatrix}$$

and

$$2 \cdot (-2, 1, 5) = (-4, 2, 10).$$

At this point it is easy to guess how one vector is subtracted from another—one simply adds individual components "algebraically." If x and y are three component vectors, then

$$x - y = \begin{pmatrix} x_1 \\ x_2 \\ x_3 \end{pmatrix} - \begin{pmatrix} y_1 \\ y_2 \\ y_3 \end{pmatrix} = \begin{pmatrix} x_1 - y_1 \\ x_2 - y_2 \\ x_3 - y_3 \end{pmatrix}.$$

1. Perform the following operations with vectors:

$$(0, 1, 5, 2) + (3, -1, 6, -1) =$$

$$\begin{pmatrix} 5 \\ 3 \end{pmatrix} + \begin{pmatrix} 2 \\ 1 \end{pmatrix} + \begin{pmatrix} -6 \\ -5 \end{pmatrix} =$$

$$3(3, 2) + 5(1, -2) =$$

$$2\begin{pmatrix} 1 \\ 2 \end{pmatrix} - 3\begin{pmatrix} 0 \\ -1 \end{pmatrix} + \begin{pmatrix} 1 \\ 1 \end{pmatrix} =$$

2. Given that vector $u = (3, 1, 0)$, vector $v = (2, -1, 5)$, and vector $w = (4, 1, -1)$, perform the following computations:

$$u + v \qquad = (\underline{}, \underline{}, \underline{})$$

$$u + v + w \quad = (\underline{}, \underline{}, \underline{})$$

$$2(u + v) - w = (\underline{}, \underline{}, \underline{}).$$

Operating with vectors is really no different than the familiar arithmetic operations with ordinary numbers. What is new is the ability to denote a whole collection of numbers by a single variable and then treat the collection as if it were a single quantity. This provides a compact, abbreviated way of dealing with many variables at once, and whole lists of problems can be represented by a single statement. Thus, the vector statement $(4, 6) - (2, 5) = (2, 1)$ is just another way of writing two separate problems, $4 - 2 = 2$ and $6 - 5 = 1$. The economy of this notation is not so apparent with vectors, but when we come to matrices, we find it a great convenience and timesaver. From one point of view, vectors and matrices are used to describe "mass-production" arithmetic, where the same operations are to be performed repeatedly on different sets of numbers. Instead of writing the three linear equations $2x + 1 = 3$, $2x - 2 = 10$, and $2x + 6 = 14$, one could simply write the vector equation:

$$2X + (1, -2, 6) = (3, 10, 14).$$

The vector $X = (1, 6, 4)$, which is the solution to this last equation, is found by solving the three equations involving the separate components. $X = (1, 6, 4)$ is a solution, as you can verify by observing that:

$$2(1, 6, 4) + (1, -2, 6) = (3, 10, 14).$$

Similarly, we can write vector equations such as $A - 3X = B$, where A and B are vectors whose components are constants, and solve for the variable vector X. The solution $X = \frac{1}{3}(A - B)$ is correct, even if A, B, and X have dozens of components. This notation gives us a way to write down a lot of arithmetic with only a few symbols.

3. In the following vector equations, solve for the vector X:

$$(3, 5) + X = (4, 7)$$ _____

$$X - \begin{pmatrix} 1 \\ 3 \\ 1 \end{pmatrix} = \begin{pmatrix} -1 \\ 2 \\ 6 \end{pmatrix}$$ _____

$$X + (a_1, a_2) = (b_1, b_2)$$ _____

$$\begin{pmatrix} 5 \\ 3 \\ 0 \end{pmatrix} + 2X - \begin{pmatrix} 3 \\ 0 \\ 1 \end{pmatrix} = \begin{pmatrix} 6 \\ 11 \\ 1 \end{pmatrix}$$ _____

$$6X + 2B - A = \begin{pmatrix} 6 \\ 5 \end{pmatrix}$$ _____

2.2 THE PRODUCT OF VECTORS

Why is it useful to have two means of representing vectors? Certainly there is little difference in the properties of row vectors and column vectors! While this is true, it is sometimes convenient to use different kinds of vectors to distinguish between different kinds of quantities that may be involved in a problem situation. In addition there is a way in which row and column vectors may be combined which is very useful in certain kinds of problems.

By way of illustration, let us imagine that a do-it-yourselfer stops at a hardware store and buys himself a can of putty, three quarts of trim paint, six gallons of outside house paint, and two new brushes. We can represent these purchases in row vector form as follows:

$x = $ (1 can of putty, 3 qts. trim paint, 6 gal. outside paint, 2 brushes)
$x = (1, 3, 6, 2)$

Now suppose that putty costs 98 cents a can, that trim paint costs $2.65 per quart, that the outside paint costs $8.20 a gallon, and that the brushes our friend selected cost $2.25 apiece. We can represent these prices in vector form also, but since *prices* are essentially different from *quantities*, let's use a column matrix:

$$y = \begin{pmatrix} .98 \\ 2.65 \\ 8.20 \\ 2.25 \end{pmatrix} \begin{matrix} \text{per can} \\ \text{per quart} \\ \text{per gallon} \\ \text{per brush} \end{matrix}$$

To find the total amount of these purchases we know that we must multiply each quantity by its respective price and then add these amounts to get the value of the total bill. And this is exactly what one does in multiplying the quantity vector x by the price vector y. The required multiplication has the following form:

$$x \cdot y = (1, 3, 6, 2) \begin{pmatrix} .98 \\ 2.65 \\ 8.20 \\ 2.25 \end{pmatrix}$$

$$= (1)(.98) + (3)(2.65) + (6)(8.20) + (2)(2.25)$$
$$= .98 + 7.95 + 49.20 + 4.50$$
$$= \$62.63.$$

This is exactly the computation that the cashier will perform in figuring our friend's bill.

The general definition of multiplication of row times column vectors is exactly like the example above: If x is a row vector and y is a column vector and each have the same number (n) of components, then the product $x \cdot y$ is defined as

$$x \cdot y = x_1y_1 + x_2y_2 \ldots + x_ny_n.$$

Vector multiplication is permitted *only* when the row vector precedes the column vector as the following examples illustrate:

$$(-1, 3, 7) \begin{pmatrix} 1 \\ 2 \\ 0 \end{pmatrix} = (-1)(1) + (3)(2) + (7)(0) = 5$$

$$(2, 0) \begin{pmatrix} 0 \\ 1 \end{pmatrix} = (2)(0) + (0)(1) = 0.$$

The result of vector multiplication is a *single number*.

 4. Multiply the vectors as shown:

$$(1, 1, -1) \cdot \begin{pmatrix} -1 \\ -1 \\ 1 \end{pmatrix} =$$

$$(1, 0, 2) \cdot \begin{pmatrix} -1 \\ 6 \\ \frac{1}{2} \end{pmatrix} =$$

2.3 OPERATIONS WITH VECTORS AND MATRICES

The vectors we have been discussing so far are really a special case of a more general concept, that of a matrix. A matrix, which we usually denote by a capital letter, say A, is written as follows:

$$A = \begin{pmatrix} a_{11} & a_{12} & . & . & . & a_{1n} \\ a_{21} & a_{22} & . & . & . & a_{2n} \\ . & . & . & . & . & . \\ . & . & . & . & . & . \\ a_{m1} & a_{m2} & . & . & . & a_{mn} \end{pmatrix}.$$

A matrix is just a rectangular array of numbers. In matrix "A" above, the numbers (or components) in the matrix are represented symbolically by the small letter "a" followed by two subscripts. The *first* subscript denotes the *row* in which the component is located, and the *second* subscript denotes the *column*. Thus a_{21} represents the number located at the intersection of the second row and the first column. The generic name a_{ij} is given to the component in the ith row and jth column. Matrix A, shown above, has a total of m rows and n columns, as you can see from the subscripts of the lower-most and rightmost component in the array, so it is called an "$m \times n$ matrix" (read as "m by n").

A special kind of matrix is the *square* matrix, so called because the number of rows equals the number of columns. Another special kind of matrix is one that has only *one* row. As we saw earlier, these are called *row vectors*. And a matrix with only *one* column—you guessed it—is called a *column vector*. Here are some examples of matrices:

2 × 3 matrix:
$$\begin{pmatrix} 5 & 2 & -3 \\ 6 & 1 & 10 \end{pmatrix}$$

4 × 2 matrix:
$$\begin{pmatrix} 5 & -12 \\ 3 & 15 \\ \frac{1}{2} & 0 \\ 16 & 9 \end{pmatrix}$$

1 × 5 matrix:
(row vector)
$$(0, 1, 2, 1, 0)$$

3 × 1 matrix:
(column vector)
$$\begin{pmatrix} 1 \\ 4 \\ 9 \end{pmatrix}$$

1 × 1 matrix: (1412)

The number 1412: 1412

2 × 2 square matrix:
$$\begin{pmatrix} 0 & -1 \\ 1 & 0 \end{pmatrix}$$

Two matrices are said to be *equal* to one another if each component of one is equal to the corresponding component of the other. Thus, if we know that

$$\begin{pmatrix} 2 & x \\ 5 & -3 \end{pmatrix} = \begin{pmatrix} 2 & 9 \\ y & -3 \end{pmatrix},$$

we could conclude that $x = 9$ and $y = 5$.

Since matrices are simply groups of numbers arranged in a special way, they can be the subject of most of the familiar arithmetic operations. The addition and multiplication of vectors were examples of these operations on the one row or one column kind of matrix. In the paragraphs to follow, some other important matrix operations will be covered, namely, the multiplication of a matrix by a number, by a vector, and by another matrix, and also the addition of matrices. Let's start with the easiest of all.

To multiply a matrix A by a constant k, one must multiply every component of A by k. The result is a new matrix kA. For example; if:

$$k = 3 \quad \text{and} \quad A = \begin{pmatrix} 2 & -1 \\ 0 & 5 \end{pmatrix},$$

then:

$$kA = 3 \cdot \begin{pmatrix} 2 & -1 \\ 0 & 5 \end{pmatrix} = \begin{pmatrix} 6 & -3 \\ 0 & 15 \end{pmatrix}.$$

There are two ways of multiplying a matrix by a vector, depending on whether the vector is a row or a column vector. As in vector multiplication, where the row vector always comes first and the column vector second, we multiply a *matrix* by a *row* vector by putting the row vector *first*, the matrix *second*. The row vector is then applied successively to the columns of the matrix, as the following example illustrates:

$$(2, 5) \cdot \begin{pmatrix} 1 & 3 \\ 3 & 9 \end{pmatrix} = \left[(2, 5) \begin{pmatrix} 1 \\ 3 \end{pmatrix}, (2, 5) \begin{pmatrix} 3 \\ 9 \end{pmatrix} \right]$$
$$= [(2 \cdot 1 + 5 \cdot 3), (2 \cdot 3 + 5 \cdot 9)]$$
$$= (17, 51).$$

The product is also a row vector whose first component is the product of the original row vector and the first column of the matrix and whose second component is the product of the original row vector and the second column of the matrix. If there were more columns in the matrix, this same procedure would be followed for as many columns as the matrix contained. Notice, however, that the number of components in the row vector must exactly equal the number of *rows* in the matrix, otherwise the multiplication is not defined.

In a similar way, we can multiply a matrix by a column vector. In this case, however, the matrix must come first and the column vector second as shown below:

$$\begin{pmatrix} 2 & 3 \\ 0 & -5 \\ -1 & 2 \end{pmatrix} \cdot \begin{pmatrix} 7 \\ 4 \end{pmatrix} = \begin{bmatrix} (\quad 2, \quad 3) \cdot \begin{pmatrix} 7 \\ 4 \end{pmatrix} \\ (\quad 0, -5) \cdot \begin{pmatrix} 7 \\ 4 \end{pmatrix} \\ (-1, \quad 2) \cdot \begin{pmatrix} 7 \\ 4 \end{pmatrix} \end{bmatrix} = \begin{pmatrix} 26 \\ -20 \\ 1 \end{pmatrix}.$$

The first component of the answer is the product of the first row of the matrix and the column vector; the second component of the answer is the product of the second row of the matrix and the column vector, and so on for as many rows as the matrix contains. In this case, the number of columns in the matrix must equal the number of components in the column vector for the multiplication operation to be defined. In the multiplication of vectors (either column or row) and matrices a simple rule applies: *multiply the row (first) by the column (second).*

 5. Before looking at an example of how one might apply these rules, here are some practice problems:

$$(0, \ 1) \begin{pmatrix} 1 & 2 \\ 3 & 4 \end{pmatrix} =$$

$$(-1, 0, +1) \begin{pmatrix} 5 & -1 \\ 3 & -3 \\ 1 & -5 \end{pmatrix} =$$

$$\begin{pmatrix} 10 & 12 \\ 5 & 4 \end{pmatrix} \begin{pmatrix} 0.20 \\ 0.25 \end{pmatrix} =$$

$$(-2) \begin{pmatrix} 1 & 15 \\ -1 & 3 \end{pmatrix} =$$

To illustrate the meaning of these operations involving vectors and matrices, consider the following situation:

There are a total of four different sump pumps marketed under the Oasis brand name. All four models have the same rating. The principal difference between models lies in the combination of accessories included. Model No. 2, for example, has no automatic shutoff control; Models 1 and 2 are shipped without mounting brackets; and so on. Production of the pumps is primarily an assembly operation. A total of five basic parts is required in various quantities depending on the model, and the manufacturer converts an order for various quantities of pumps into orders on his vendors for the proper number of parts. (This is the familiar "parts explosion" problem in its simplest form.)

Suppose he has orders for 3 Model 1 pumps, 5 Model 2's, 2 Model 3's, and 10 Model 4's. He can write this *total order* as the row vector

$$(3, 5, 2, 10) .$$

From the parts list, he can construct the following matrix in which each component is the number of parts of each type (represented by the columns) required by each model (represented by the rows):

$$
\begin{array}{c}
\textit{Part type} \\
\\
\textit{Pump} \\
\textit{Model}
\end{array}
\begin{array}{c}
 \\
1 \\
2 \\
3 \\
4
\end{array}
\begin{pmatrix}
1 & 2 & 3 & 4 & 5 \\
1 & 2 & 0 & 5 & 2 \\
0 & 3 & 0 & 1 & 5 \\
1 & 1 & 4 & 2 & 2 \\
1 & 2 & 4 & 5 & 5
\end{pmatrix}
$$

Thus, a Model 2 pump requires 3 of part number 2, one part number 4, and 5 part 5's, reading across the second row of the matrix.

To find out how many of each part is needed to fill the order represented by the row vector written earlier, the manufacturer needs only to compute the product

$$
(3, 5, 2, 10)
\begin{pmatrix}
1 & 2 & 0 & 5 & 2 \\
0 & 3 & 0 & 1 & 5 \\
1 & 1 & 4 & 2 & 2 \\
1 & 2 & 4 & 5 & 5
\end{pmatrix}
$$

$$= (3 \cdot 1 + 5 \cdot 0 + 2 \cdot 1 + 10 \cdot 1, \ 3 \cdot 2 + 5 \cdot 3 + 2 \cdot 1 + 10 \cdot 2, \text{ etc.})$$

$$= (15, 43, 48, 74, 85).$$

The result of the multiplication is a row vector with 5 components, each of which represents the total number of parts of the type corresponding to the original column headings needed to fill the order. In other words, he needs 43 part 2's: 6 for the 3 Model 1 pumps, 15 for the 5 Model 2 pumps, and so on.

Actually, the multiplication of each column of the matrix by the row (or order quantity) vector is exactly equivalent to the ordinary arithmetic a person who had never heard of vectors or matrices would use in solving this problem. The advantage of the matrix notation is that the entire procedure can be conveniently described and kept straight regardless of how big the problem gets. (As we shall see a little later this is a bigger advantage than appears obvious at first. In fact, it is for exactly this same reason that we find ordinary algebra helpful.)

At this point, however, let's take the Oasis pump people a step further into matrix algebra. Suppose we represent the unit prices of the various parts as a *column* vector.

$$Part\ No.$$

$$
\begin{array}{cc}
1 \\
2 \\
3 \\
4 \\
5
\end{array}
\quad
\begin{pmatrix}
28.00 \\
11.50 \\
3.45 \\
0.90 \\
6.75
\end{pmatrix}
$$

The question is, how much will it cost to buy the parts to fill the total order? Consider the product

$$
\begin{pmatrix}
1 & 2 & 0 & 5 & 2 \\
0 & 3 & 0 & 1 & 5 \\
1 & 1 & 4 & 2 & 2 \\
1 & 2 & 4 & 5 & 5
\end{pmatrix}
\begin{pmatrix}
28.00 \\
11.50 \\
3.45 \\
0.90 \\
6.75
\end{pmatrix}
$$

$$
=
\begin{pmatrix}
1(28.00) + 2(11.50) + 0(3.45) + 5(0.90) + 2(6.75) \\
\text{etc.} \\
1(28.00) + 2(11.50) + 4(3.45) + 5(0.90) + 5(6.75)
\end{pmatrix}
$$

$$
=
\begin{pmatrix}
69.00 \\
69.15 \\
68.60 \\
103.05
\end{pmatrix}
$$

The resulting 4-component column vector represents the material cost of parts for one model pump. Thus the parts for a single Model 4 pump cost $103.05.

The next step is to multiply this column vector by the order quantity row vector to determine the cost of the total order.

$$
(3,\ 5,\ 2,\ 10)
\begin{pmatrix}
69.00 \\
69.15 \\
68.60 \\
103.05
\end{pmatrix}
= \$1{,}720.45.
$$

And this is the total cost of all parts for the complete order. But notice that we might have done this another way. Since we had earlier determined the total number of each part (the five-component row vector), why not multiply this by the part-price vector as follows:

$$
(15,\ 43,\ 48,\ 74,\ 85)
\begin{pmatrix}
28.00 \\
11.50 \\
3.45 \\
0.90 \\
6.75
\end{pmatrix}
= \$1{,}720.45.
$$

The same answer as before! As a matter of fact we could have done the whole job at once:

$$(3, 5, 2, 10) \begin{pmatrix} 1 & 2 & 0 & 5 & 2 \\ 0 & 3 & 0 & 1 & 5 \\ 1 & 1 & 4 & 2 & 2 \\ 1 & 2 & 4 & 5 & 5 \end{pmatrix} \begin{pmatrix} 28.00 \\ 11.50 \\ 3.45 \\ 0.90 \\ 6.75 \end{pmatrix} = \$1,720.45.$$

The product is of the form xMy, where x is a row vector, M is a matrix, and y is a column vector; and we got the same answer two different ways by choosing two ways of performing the multiplication, namely:

$$xMy = (xM)y \text{ or } x(My).$$

2.4 ADDITION AND MULTIPLICATION OF MATRICES

Two matrices can be added providing they have the same dimensions, that is, if one is a 3 × 5 matrix, then the other must likewise be a 3 × 5 matrix. (The first figure in the dimension identifies the number of rows, the second figure identifies the number of columns. A 3 × 5 matrix, therefore, has 3 rows and 5 columns.) The sum of two matrices is found by adding corresponding components, as in the example below.

$$\begin{pmatrix} 1 & -2 & 3 \\ 4 & -9 & -3 \end{pmatrix} + \begin{pmatrix} 0 & 3 & -5 \\ -6 & 1 & 3 \end{pmatrix} = \begin{pmatrix} 1 & 1 & -2 \\ -2 & -8 & 0 \end{pmatrix}.$$

Multiplication of matrices is only slightly more involved. To illustrate, let us again use a numerical example and begin by defining matrices

$$A = \begin{pmatrix} 1 & 5 & 0 \\ 2 & 3 & 1 \end{pmatrix}$$

and

$$B = \begin{pmatrix} 3 & 4 \\ 0 & 1 \\ 2 & -1 \end{pmatrix}.$$

The required multiplication is performed as follows:

$$AB = \begin{pmatrix} 1 & 5 & 0 \\ 2 & 3 & 1 \end{pmatrix} \begin{pmatrix} 3 & 4 \\ 0 & 1 \\ 2 & -1 \end{pmatrix}$$

$$= \begin{pmatrix} 1\cdot3 + 5\cdot0 + 0\cdot2, & 1\cdot4 + 5\cdot1 + 0\cdot(-1) \\ 2\cdot3 + 3\cdot0 + 1\cdot2, & 2\cdot4 + 3\cdot1 + 1\cdot(-1) \end{pmatrix}$$

$$= \begin{pmatrix} 3 & 9 \\ 8 & 10 \end{pmatrix}.$$

Notice that each entry in the new matrix is the product of one of the *rows of A* times one of the *columns of B*. The component in the second row first column of the new matrix, for example, is the product of two vectors—the second row of *A* times the first column of *B* as indicated below:

$$\begin{pmatrix} 1 & 5 & 0 \\ 2 & 3 & 1 \end{pmatrix} \begin{pmatrix} 3 & 4 \\ 0 & 1 \\ 2 & -1 \end{pmatrix} = \begin{pmatrix} 3 & 9 \\ 8 & 10 \end{pmatrix}.$$

This leads to a general rule for determining any component in the product matrix: The component in the *i*th row and *j*th column of the matrix *AB* is the product of the *i*th row of *A* times the *j*th column of *B*.

6. Draw lines through the rows and columns that are multiplied to produce the circled component in the product matrix.

$$\begin{pmatrix} a & a \\ a & a \end{pmatrix} \begin{pmatrix} b & b \\ b & b \end{pmatrix} = \begin{pmatrix} c & c \\ c & \textcircled{c} \end{pmatrix}$$

$$\begin{pmatrix} a & a & a \\ a & a & a \\ a & a & a \end{pmatrix} \begin{pmatrix} b \\ b \\ b \end{pmatrix} = \begin{pmatrix} c \\ c \\ \textcircled{c} \end{pmatrix}$$

$$(a \quad a) \begin{pmatrix} b & b & b & b \\ b & b & b & b \end{pmatrix} = (c \quad c \quad \textcircled{c} \quad c)$$

From the exercise above the dimensions of the matrices *A* and *B* and the product matrix *AB* are as follows:

A	B	AB
2×2	2×2	2×2
3×3	3×1	3×1
1×2	2×4	1×4

Notice that the number of *columns* in *A* and the number of *rows* in *B* are equal. This, in fact, is a necessary condition in order to be able to multiply matrix *A* by matrix *B*. Notice also that the resulting product matrix *AB* has the same number of *rows* as *A* and same number of *columns* as *B*. In general, if matrix *A* has the dimensions $a \times b$ and matrix *B* has the dimensions $c \times d$, the following rules apply:

1. The two matrices can be multiplied only if $b = c$,
   i.e., $(a \times b)(c \times d)$ is allowed if $b = c$.
2. The product matrix will have dimensions $(a \times d)$, i.e.,
$$(a \times b)(c \times d) = (a \times d)$$

It was mentioned earlier that a special kind of matrix was the square matrix, i.e., one that has the same number of rows as it has columns. Let us now consider some of the properties that make these "special." In the first place a square matrix passes the requirements above for multiplication by itself. This makes it possible to define an operation of raising these matrices to powers. For example, if

$$A = \begin{pmatrix} 2 & 0 \\ 1 & 4 \end{pmatrix},$$

then

$$A^2 = A \cdot A = \begin{pmatrix} 2 & 0 \\ 1 & 4 \end{pmatrix} \begin{pmatrix} 2 & 0 \\ 1 & 4 \end{pmatrix} = \begin{pmatrix} 4 & 0 \\ 6 & 16 \end{pmatrix}.$$

Another unique characteristic is that any two square matrices of the same dimensions can be multiplied in *either* order. Given matrix A and matrix B—and for simplicity let's assume they both have the dimension 2 × 2—we can multiply in the order AB or BA. In ordinary algebra, of course, the result is the same either way. But what about matrix algerba? Let's try it and find out.

$$A = \begin{pmatrix} 1 & 3 \\ 2 & 4 \end{pmatrix} \qquad B = \begin{pmatrix} 1 & 2 \\ 3 & 4 \end{pmatrix}$$

$$AB = \begin{pmatrix} 1 & 3 \\ 2 & 4 \end{pmatrix} \begin{pmatrix} 1 & 2 \\ 3 & 4 \end{pmatrix} = \begin{pmatrix} 10 & 14 \\ 14 & 20 \end{pmatrix}$$

$$BA = \begin{pmatrix} 1 & 2 \\ 3 & 4 \end{pmatrix} \begin{pmatrix} 1 & 3 \\ 2 & 4 \end{pmatrix} = \begin{pmatrix} 5 & 11 \\ 11 & 25 \end{pmatrix}$$

From this it is clear that *AB does not necessarily* equal *BA*.

7. Of the following matrices, multiply those that *can be* multiplied.

$$\begin{pmatrix} 1 & 3 & 5 \\ 2 & 0 & 1 \end{pmatrix} \begin{pmatrix} 2 & 0 \\ 1 & 5 \\ 6 & 2 \end{pmatrix} =$$

$$\begin{pmatrix} 3 & 2 \\ 4 & 1 \end{pmatrix} \begin{pmatrix} 1 & 2 & 1 \\ 3 & 0 & 2 \\ -1 & 5 & 0 \end{pmatrix} =$$

$$\begin{pmatrix} 4 & 0 & 5 \\ 0 & 1 & -6 \\ 3 & 0 & 4 \end{pmatrix} \begin{pmatrix} 4 & 0 & -5 \\ -18 & 1 & 24 \\ -3 & 0 & 4 \end{pmatrix} =$$

3. Applications of Vectors and Matrices

3.1 AN APPLICATION OF MATRICES IN GOZINTO PROBLEMS

A common business problem which must be solved before shop scheduling can be accomplished is the parts list problem or parts explosion, as it is often called. On page 184 we illustrated a very simple example of this problem at the Oasis Pump Company, but in the manufacture of a typical product, there will be finished assemblies, one or more levels of subassemblies, and finally detail parts. In order to translate a demand for finished assemblies into a production or purchasing schedule for detail parts and subassemblies, it is essential that a means of recording the assembly breakdown be available. In other words, each part that goes into each assembly must be noted, for every assembly level. If the product is at all complex, the ordering activity is often divided among several organizational groups, each of manageable size and with its own specific area of responsibility. *If all goes well,* coordination among these groups will eliminate scheduling and time sequencing problems so that each individual part gets ordered in the right quantity, at the right time, and without duplications and omissions. For this reason there is much interest in new systems capable of handling the parts explosion and ordering task more or less automatically. Such systems, however, require new concepts.

According to Andrew Vazsonyi, who writes on this subject in his book *Scientific Programming in Business and Industry,*[2] the basic concepts in this area were developed by the celebrated Italian mathematician Zepartzat Gozinto. Since the *Collected Works of Z. Gozinto* are still in preparation, we cannot explore his theories in depth. Suffice it to say that matrix operations are the key to the entire theory insofar as it applies to the parts list problem.

As an example, suppose a factory were to make three finished products, designated P1, P2 and P3. Suppose further that four intermediate subassemblies were involved, designated A1, A2, A3 and A4, and two detail parts designated D1 and D2. Suppose that the rules for assembly are as shown in the *Gozinto graph*.

---

[2] The Gozinto Graph on page 191 and the logical structure of the problem described in this paragraph have been adapted from Andrew Vazsonyi, *Scientific Programming in Business and Industry* (New York: John Wiley & Sons, Inc., 1958), pp. 429–39.

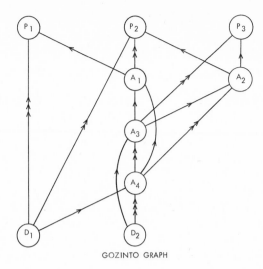

GOZINTO GRAPH

As the Gozinto graph shows, product P2 is assembled from two D1's (two arrowheads between D1 and P2), two A1's, and one A2. Each of these A1's in turn is assembled from one A3 and one A4. Also the A1 subassembly is used along with three D1's to make P1. And so it goes, with all the Gozinto relationships as shown. Even in such a simple case as this, with only nine part numbers, the graph can get very complicated.

Suppose a forecast calls for producing 20 P1's, 25 P2's, and 35 P3's. Someone must determine how many of each of the subassemblies to produce, and how many of the detail parts are to be made or bought. A typical question to get this calculation started might be "how many D2's does it take to make one P2?"

 8. By looking at the Gozinto graph, answer the question just posed.

Answer: _____ D2's in one P2.

Answering such questions as this can get to be terribly difficult in actual cases; with a thousand parts it is impossible for practical purposes without some method of systematizing the computation. That is where matrices come in.

The first step in developing the total requirements for a given production schedule is to construct the *Next Assembly Quantity Matrix*. Each entry in this matrix, which has as many rows and columns as there are part numbers, is a number which shows how many of the (row) part are used directly in each (column) part. In our example, the number located at the intersection of row D1

BASIC MATHEMATICS

and column P2 would be 2, because two D1's are used *directly* in each P2. Note that D1's go into A4's, which in turn go into A2's, which in turn go into P2 also, but this is an *indirect* use of D1. The Next Assembly Quantity Matrix for the entire graph is:

	P1	P2	P3	A1‑	A2	A3	A4	D1	D2
P1	0	0	0	0	0	0	0	0	0
P2	0	0	0	0	0	0	0	0	0
P3	0	0	0	0	0	0	0	0	0
A1	1	2	0	0	0	0	0	0	0
A2	0	1	1	0	0	0	0	0	0
A3	0	0	2	1	1	0	0	0	0
A4	0	0	0	1	2	2	0	0	0
D1	3	2	0	0	0	0	1	0	0
D2	0	0	0	0	0	1	3	0	0

Note that the P1, P2, and P3 rows are all zeros, because none of them gozinto any parts. Also, the columns D1 and D2 are all zeros, because no part gozinto them.

Our goal is to answer all questions of the form "how many x go into each y?" With the aid of matrix theory, a digital computer if the problem is very large, and the Next Assembly Quantity Matrix, these questions can all be answered easily and simultaneously. To understand the way this is done requires a new concept: the *inverse* of a square matrix.

A special matrix called the *identity* matrix is a matrix with *ones* along the principal (upper left to lower right) diagonal, and *zeros* everywhere else. For example, the 4×4 identity matrix looks like:

$$\begin{pmatrix} 1 & 0 & 0 & 0 \\ 0 & 1 & 0 & 0 \\ 0 & 0 & 1 & 0 \\ 0 & 0 & 0 & 1 \end{pmatrix}$$

Denote this matrix by the letter I. The *inverse* of a square matrix A is now defined as that matrix which, when multiplied by A, gives the matrix I. The inverse of A is usually denoted by the symbol A^{-1}, so that the definition, in shorthand, is:

$$A^{-1}A = I.$$

It is easy to see the analogy between this idea and the notion of a *reciprocal* in ordinary arithmetic, for the reciprocal of a number (like 20, say) is the number to multiply 20 by to get 1, i.e., the reciprocal of 20 is 1/20 or 0.05, for $(.05)(20) = 1$.

Two matrices whose product is the identity matrix were given as an exercise in section 2.4 of this chapter. The multiplication was:

$$\begin{pmatrix} 4 & 0 & 5 \\ 0 & 1 & -6 \\ 3 & 0 & 4 \end{pmatrix} \begin{pmatrix} 4 & 0 & -5 \\ -18 & 1 & 24 \\ -3 & 0 & 4 \end{pmatrix} = \begin{pmatrix} 1 & 0 & 0 \\ 0 & 1 & 0 \\ 0 & 0 & 1 \end{pmatrix}.$$

Thus, the first matrix on the left side of the equation is the inverse of the second.

There are systematic procedures for finding the inverse of a square matrix. Most of these procedures are rather involved and, in fact, are seldom performed manually. Instead, matrix inversion computer programs exist for almost every type of machine, and people working with matrices just put data on the matrix through a standard library program to get their answer. For example, the following 2×2 matrix has an inverse as shown:

$$A = \begin{pmatrix} 4 & 1 \\ 3 & 2 \end{pmatrix} \qquad A^{-1} = \begin{pmatrix} 0.4 & -0.2 \\ -0.6 & 0.8 \end{pmatrix}.$$

A quick check shows that the product $A^{-1}A$ is the 2×2 identity matrix, as required.

Before returning to the Gozinto problem, suppose we use the idea of an inverse in solving simultaneous linear equations. On page 93 (in Chapter 4), we displayed the solution of the following set of equations:

$$4x + y = 10$$
$$3x + 2y = 5.$$

The solution was $x = 3$ and $y = -2$. Rewriting this set of equations using vectors and matrices:

$$\begin{pmatrix} 4 & 1 \\ 3 & 2 \end{pmatrix} \begin{pmatrix} x \\ y \end{pmatrix} = \begin{pmatrix} 10 \\ 5 \end{pmatrix}.$$

The 2×2 matrix on the left (called a *matrix of coefficients*) is formed, as the name implies, by the coefficients of x and y in the original two equations. The variables, x and y, and the right-hand side are both written as column vectors. Just to make certain this is all legal, let's perform the multiplication on the left-hand side of the equal sign.

$$\begin{pmatrix} 4 & 1 \\ 3 & 2 \end{pmatrix} \begin{pmatrix} x \\ y \end{pmatrix} = \begin{pmatrix} 4x + y \\ 3x + 2y \end{pmatrix}.$$

Setting this equal to the vector

$$\begin{pmatrix} 10 \\ 5 \end{pmatrix},$$

is exactly equivalent to the original two equations since the equal sign, you recall, implies componentwise equality.

Since we have already denoted the 2×2 matrix above by the letter A and found its inverse, we can rewrite this set of equations as:

$$A\begin{pmatrix} x \\ y \end{pmatrix} = \begin{pmatrix} 10 \\ 5 \end{pmatrix}.$$

To solve this matrix equation, we multiply both sides by the same thing, namely the inverse of A, i.e., A^{-1}.

$$A^{-1}A\begin{pmatrix} x \\ y \end{pmatrix} = A^{-1}\begin{pmatrix} 10 \\ 5 \end{pmatrix}.$$

But $A^{-1}A = I$, so the left-hand side of the above equation reduces to

$$I\begin{pmatrix} x \\ y \end{pmatrix}.$$

This again reduces to simply

$$\begin{pmatrix} x \\ y \end{pmatrix},$$

since the column vector is not changed in value by multiplication by the identity matrix, I. Hence the solution is

$$\begin{pmatrix} x \\ y \end{pmatrix} = A^{-1}\begin{pmatrix} 10 \\ 5 \end{pmatrix}.$$

In other words, if we could find A^{-1} conveniently, we could perform the multiplication on the right, ending up with a column vector whose components would be just the desired unknown values of x and y. Using the actual inverse of A found previously:

$$\begin{pmatrix} x \\ y \end{pmatrix} = \begin{pmatrix} 0.4 & -0.2 \\ -0.6 & 0.8 \end{pmatrix} \begin{pmatrix} 10 \\ 5 \end{pmatrix} = \begin{pmatrix} 3 \\ -2 \end{pmatrix},$$

which is the same solution found before.

The full value of matrix notation is realized in the *algebra of matrices*, of which the previous discussion is just a sample. Elementary algebra deals with symbols standing for numbers; the algebra of matrices deals with symbols standing for matrices. Although the rules are slightly different (back on page 189 we found that $AB \neq BA$ if A and B are matrices) the same sort of manipulation is possible. The matrix containing all zeros acts just like the number zero in elementary algebra, and the identity matrix corresponds to the number one, as we have already pointed out.

The Gozinto problem is solved using the algebra of matrices. Imagine for a moment a matrix, call it X, whose elements are the *total* requirement of the row part for each of the column parts. Denoting the Next Assembly Quantity Matrix, already constructed from the Gozinto Graph, by the symbol N, it turns out that the following matrix equation can be shown to hold:

$$X = NX + I.$$

This equation can be solved for the unknown matrix X, as follows:

$$X - NX = I$$
$$IX - NX = I \qquad (\text{since } IX = X)$$
$$(I - N)X = I$$
$$(I - N)^{-1}(I - N)X = (I - N)^{-1}I$$
$$IX = (I - N)^{-1}I$$
$$X = (I - N)^{-1}.$$

Thus, if one forms a new matrix $(I - N)$ by subtracting the known Next Assembly Quantity Matrix from the identity matrix, and then finds the inverse of this new matrix, he will have the desired Total Parts Requirement Matrix. Because matrix inversion by computer has received so much attention as a useful tool, a lot of shortcuts have been developed. For a large Gozinto-type problem, by taking advantage of these shortcuts and some clever tricks associated with setting up the problem, solutions for the Total Parts Requirement Matrix can be found even for cases with thousands of parts. In this example, the inverse of $(I - N)$ was found in 5 seconds of computer time using a GE 235 computer. The result is the unknown matrix X which turns out to be:

	P1	P2	P3	A1	A2	A3	A4	D1	D2
P1	1	0	0	0	0	0	0	0	0
P2	0	1	0	0	0	0	0	0	0
P3	0	0	1	0	0	0	0	0	0
A1	1	2	0	1	0	0	0	0	0
A2	0	1	1	0	1	0	0	0	0
A3	1	3	3	1	1	1	0	0	0
A4	3	10	8	3	4	2	1	0	0
D1	6	12	8	3	4	2	1	1	0
D2	10	33	27	10	13	7	3	0	1

This matrix reveals at a glance how many of each part are required for a schedule. For example, each A3 requires 2-A4, 2-D1 and 7-D2. Note that according to the Gozinto graph, one A3 is built from 2-A4 and 1-D2; the 2-A4 require 2-D1 and 6-D2 at the lower level of assembly.

3.2 OTHER USES OF MATRICES

After discussing the emergence of decision making as a quantitative methodology, the author of a recent text concluded that "matrix algebra is now considered *the* algebra for management people who are interested in scientific decision making." Few people today are prepared to agree or disagree; for that matter, not many would consider such a statement worthy of comment. Of interest, however, are the facts motivating such a conclusion; and one fact that is hard to ignore is the growth in the number of business applications of matrix concepts.

In this chapter, after describing the basic matrix operations, we discussed only two uses: one was the gozinto problem, the other (and then only in passing) was the important application of matrices in the solution of simultaneous linear equations. But this hardly does justice to the endless variety of possibilities that exist in the business setting. For example, let's consider the potential that matrix algebra might hold in a completely different area of business activity not even remotely associated with gozinto problems or simultaneous equations. How about double-entry bookkeeping?

Assuming that you already have some familiarity with this subject, we shall point out only those aspects of double-entry bookkeeping that are relevant to our discussion. First, two records are made of each transaction. The amount of the transaction is classified (according to account) and recorded once as a *debit*, then the same amount is classified and recorded as a *credit*. It is not difficult in such a system to record by accident two debits or two credits or to neglect completely the second, or offsetting, record. The books are said to be in balance when the sum of the debits equals the sum of the credits. Barring errors, this condition will exist; but, since errors are possible, the *trial balance* is a means of verification.

Now let us describe another system; a system in which a transaction is doubly classified, but recorded only once. Imagine, if you will, a ledger in the form of a matrix in which the individual accounts have been arranged in rows and columns. The rows represent accounts to be credited and the columns, the accounts to be debited. A transaction such as Cost of Sales, for example, would be recorded as a debit to the Cost of Sales account (represented by a column) and as a credit to Inventory (represented by one of the rows). Since the record is entered only once—at the intersection of the appropriate row and column—the common errors of the double entry system mentioned above are avoided; and the need for taking trial balances for the purpose of detecting these kinds of errors is eliminated.

For the sake of simplicity let's assume that we had only 5 accounts in our ledger. Our new ledger, then, could be represented as a 5×5 matrix, call it matrix L. Suppose we now define the vector b as a row vector containing 5 ones, i.e., $b = (1, 1, 1, 1, 1)$. The product bL would be a row vector whose components represent the debit balances of each account.

$$bL = \left(\begin{array}{l} \text{a row vector representing} \\ \text{the debit balances by account} \end{array} \right).$$

By defining a column vector c, also having 5 ones, the product Lc would give us

$$Lc = \left(\begin{array}{l} \text{a column} \\ \text{vector} \\ \text{representing} \\ \text{the credit} \\ \text{balances by} \\ \text{account} \end{array} \right).$$

And multiplying the row vector (bL) by c would produce the number representing the sum of the debit balances, i.e.,

$$(bL)c = \text{Total Debit Balance.}$$

This same number, of course, is also the total credit balance.

We could go on to demonstrate other advantages of our matrix ledger. For instance, the balance sheet and operating statement information requirements are easily generated by matrix operations. The point here, however, is strictly to illustrate a possible use of matrix algebra and not to suggest a need to change our bookkeeping methods. The drawbacks of this matrix system are fairly obvious. For example, many transactions may have to be recorded in a single cell which is certainly unwieldy. Also, there are usually hundreds of accounts and subaccounts which would require the physical size of the transaction matrix to exceed reasonable limits. Furthermore, it is often necessary to find the sum of the debits and the sum of the credits in a given account. If each cell in the transaction matrix became a "page" in a ledger, the simple task of adding the entries in a row or in a column of the matrix would become the forbidding task of looking up and adding the numbers recorded on many different pages of the ledger. For these reasons, the double-entry system, in spite of its shortcomings and the necessity for trial balances, is usually preferable for a large "pencil and paper" bookkeeping system.

However, equipment which has the capacity to store the information contained in a large number of cells, and which permits rapid retrieval of the information in any one or a whole series of cells, is ideally suited to handle the double-classification system of bookkeeping described above. Thus, high-speed electronic computers have made possible the use of such matrix-based systems in accounting work.

Our objective in this chapter has been simply to introduce the notion of matrices. Before we leave this topic perhaps it is possible to illustrate one of the reasons why matrices have so many applications and why this is indeed an extensive notion. Recall the Gozinto graph. This graph is just one case of a more general class of mathematical structures called "linear graphs." A linear graph is just a collection of points with arrows connecting them in various ways. The standard organization chart is a linear graph. So is a critical path scheduling network. The "decision trees" of probability theory are linear graphs. What is even more important to one who knows matrices is the following fact: A linear graph is *exactly equivalent* to a matrix! In other words, one who knows a great deal about matrices already is an expert in graph theory, too. No extra charge. Our discussion of matrices could also be continued to show, for example, the role they play in such subjects as probability theory, Markov processes, queuing (waiting line) theory, regression theory, game theory, linear and other forms of mathematical programing, and so on. For those interested in such further uses of matrices there are many excellent reference texts available.

CHAPTER 8

The Algebra of Sets

1. Introduction

1.1 NEW NAMES FOR OLD

Sometimes, when starting the study of a new subject, we find to our surprise that we already have a good deal of informal experience with its content, even though the formal vocabulary of the subject may sound a bit strange.

This is certainly the case with *set theory*, and the *algebra of sets* especially. You and everyone you know have been dealing with the ingredients of the subject all your lives; the principles of this branch of mathematics have been the foundations of your thinking processes. Many of the more subtle aspects of the theory are incorporated unconsciously, yet most of us are completely unaware of the theory itself.

Ten years ago, set theory at most universities was a postgraduate course usually taken by math majors. Now, the elements of this branch of mathematics are being taught to children as early as the first grade of elementary school. Thus, this last chapter is directed to those of us who were not math majors in graduate school or were just born too soon. The theory does have important uses in itself, but the greatest benefits will be in the increased understanding of other important areas of mathematics, which result from knowing about sets and their algebra.

1.2 WHAT IS SET THEORY ABOUT?

The theory of sets is about sets—just as the theory of numbers is about numbers. The word "set" is already familiar; a set is simply a collection of things. The things may be tangible, like a set of books, or intangible, a set of rules. For some strange reason, when adults are introduced to the notion of a set, and then told that there is a whole branch of mathematics to be learned, they find it hard to believe. What's to say about a concept so simple as "a collection of things"? Yet they do not find it surprising that a tremendous amount of mathematical theory exists which concerns itself with the very elementary concept of number. As it turns out, the algebra of sets (which speaks about collections of things) is *less* complicated than the algebra of numbers (which talks about only the "howmanyness" of such collections). In fact, if one learned the algebra of sets *first* (as our young children are doing) the "regular" algebra of numbers would be much easier to learn, understand, and use.

When speaking (in English) about sets, we use many words which are the commonest in the whole language. Examples are: "thing," "sort," "by," "from," "to," "same," "is," "some," "the," "it," "with," "has," "a," etc. Most third graders are already using such words every day. Some other words are more technical and have special meanings in set theory. Words like "property," "relation," "sorting," "selection," "choose," "match,' "collate," "group," "classify," "merge," "correspondence," "elements," etc., may be already familiar to you.

Because of the possible ambiguity of such words, however, people working in set theory have invented symbols and given them precise meanings. As a result of such precision of definition, clarity is achieved in the expression of common ideas. Even more important, it becomes possible to express with clarity many of the ideas which are "hard to think about" clearly. Through mathematical symbolism, it is possible to deal explicitly and carefully with these ideas, and solve problems using well-defined rules (the rules of the algebra of sets) which our minds could not otherwise handle.

Thus set theory is about sets, and the algebra of sets is a set (!) of symbols and relations between them. The algebra of sets is often referred to as *Boolean algebra,* in honor of a great English mathematician, George Boole (1815–64), who in 1854 published a book called *The Investigation of the Laws of Thought.* In this book, Boole described the major aspects of a new algebra especially adapted to handling classes (sets) and propositions. Boole's ambition was not in the least modest, as these words from his first chapter indicate:

The design of the following treatise is to investigate the fundamental laws of those operations of the mind by which reasoning is performed; to give expression to them in the symbolical language of a Calculus; and upon this foundation to establish the science of logic and construct its method: to make that method itself the basis of general methods for the application of the mathematical doctrine of the Probabilities; and, finally, to collect from the various elements of truth brought to view in the course of these inquiries some probable intimations concerning the nature and the constitution of the human mind.

Nevertheless, it must be admitted that it has taken nearly a hundred years for T. C. Mits to become acquainted with this algebra and its uses. So far, the most important *direct* uses of the modern version of Boolean algebra have been in the field of switches, circuits, signals, controls, and computers—all of which are involved in the design of so-called "intelligent" machines, such as those which compute, process data, simulate, analyze, or control automatically. Also, the algebra of sets has become the recognized language of *symbolic logic,* which is finding growing application in many fields. More and more, the fundamental ideas of many branches of mathematics are being stated in the language of sets—for example, probability theory is now based almost completely on set theory.

Perhaps an even better way to get an idea just what Boolean algebra is about is to see a problem which is hard to do "in your head" but straightforward for Boolean algebra. Consider the following situation:

The by-laws of a certain company require: (1) that the Board of Directors appoint from among its members a Financial Committee; (2) that no one shall serve on both the Board of Directors and the Appropriations Council unless they are also on the Financial Committee; (3) that no member of Appropriations Council shall be on the Financial Committee.

On the basis of these rules, make a judgment on the following:

1. Is the following statement true or false? "A member of the Board of Directors may serve on the Appropriations Council." Circle one: T   F

Note in this example that the original three rules mention three different classes (sets) of persons (the Board, the Council, and the Committee) a total of seven times. It is possible, as we will see in section 2.3 of this chapter, to replace these rules with two much simpler rules. In general, one of the things which can be done with Boolean algebra is to take groups of rules or conditions (like contract terms or legal documents or tax provisions, etc.) and manipulate them into forms that are logically equivalent or logically implied. This can be done rigorously, directly and easily—if not manually, then by putting such calculations on a computer, which might even be programed to answer questions ("Is it legal to—?") directly.

1.3 COMPARISON WITH ORDINARY ALGEBRA

The ordinary algebra which we have discussed in earlier chapters deals with:

Elements: the numbers, and the symbols which stand for them
Operations: the rules for operating on the elements, such as addition, division, raising to powers, etc.,

plus an assortment of other ideas such as equation, inequality, solving for the unknown, and so on. This algebra has come to be called *elementary* algebra, not because all of its problems are considered to be elementary, but rather because mathematicians needed some way to distinguish it from all the *other* algebras. Besides elementary algebra, there are algebras of fields, of rings, of ideals, of matrices, of groups, of sets, of lattices, and even some with names like Linear Associative Algebra.

In the same way as elementary algebra, Boolean algebra deals with elements and operations, but different ones. The elements are *sets* instead of numbers, and the operations are *union, intersection, complementation, inclusion,* etc., instead of addition, multiplication, and so on. When first learned, set theory seems simple, because it *is* simple. Actually, *elementary* algebra is really so *complicated* that it took the human race centuries to develop a really good symbolism to deal with the numerical problems which confronted it. The subject matter of the algebra of sets, on the other hand, is so *simple* that man has muddled along for centuries without even realizing a need for symbolism. The time has come now to learn some of the new symbols and their meanings.

2.   Basic Ideas of Set Theory

2.1 SETS AND SUBSETS

A well-defined collection of objects is known as a *set*. This is an abstract concept—the objects do not have to be real objects, they can be ideas or anything one chooses. It is not possible to define the concept of a set in terms of any simpler concepts, because no simpler concepts have been thought of yet. Also, the *concept* of a set is completely independent of what the set *consists* of. A set of books is *not* the books themselves. This allows a person to talk about the set rather than the books comprising the set, just as a person can talk about his family without mentioning the names of anyone in it.

The various pieces of furniture in a room form a set. So do all the persons on a company's payroll at some particular moment. So do all the persons who ever have been or ever will be employed by the company. So do all the ideas that mankind has ever had, or all the human beings who will have ever lived between 1,000,000 B.C. and 1,000,000 A.D. The only requirement is that the collection of things included in the set be *well defined,* that is, that a way is given by which it can be definitely determined whether *any* object is or is not a member of the collection. If such a way exists, then the collection is called a *set.*

There are just two basic ways to specify a set. Keeping in mind the definition above, it is easy to see that the defining property (which well defines the set) can be simply (1) a listing of the names of every member of the set, or (2) it can be some sort of a rule which can be applied rigorously to every object in all creation. The first of these is called a *listing* of the set, the second is called a *description* of the set.

For example, the set of all companies who manufacture computers is usually specified as a listing: Control Data, General Electric, IBM, Honeywell, etc. A listing which represents a set is written with braces {. . .}. The "big three" automotive companies, therefore, would be designated as {GM, Ford, Chrysler}, likewise, the set of all even integers between 5 and 13 would be designated as {6, 8, 10, 12}.

Sets are more often specified with descriptions, i.e., one or more rules which permit determining whether any object is or is not a member of the set. Such a description is "All U.S. Corporations whose stock was listed on the New York Stock Exchange on December 31, 1964." It would be clumsy to specify this set with a listing like {Abbott Laboratories . . . , etc., because it would take several pages of paper to get to: . . . , Zenith Radio}. Similarly, it is easier to say "all the even integers between 1 and 999,999" than to try to list them. Sometimes it is not possible to list the elements of a set, as you would easily discover for yourself if you would try to list the set "all positive integers greater than 1" (which has infinitely many members, i.e., is an infinite set), or the set "all satellites to be launched during the next three years" (whose members we aren't able to list in advance). In other words, some sets *must* be described by rules.

A set that consists entirely of some members of another set is called a *subset* of that other set. Thus {Washington, Lincoln, Jefferson} is a subset of the set of all U.S. Presidents, {2, 3.15, π, e} is a subset of the set of all numbers, and "the set of all even integers" is a subset of "the set of all integers." Notice that the integer 5 is not a subset of the set of all integers, but the set {5} is such a subset. To be as careful as mathematicians must, it is necessary to distinguish between an *object* and the *set* containing just that one object. This may seem a bit picayune, but it is no more so than distinguishing between a doughnut and the space occupied by the doughnut. The space is doughnut-shaped, and the doughnut just fits into it nicely, but they are not the same thing. We can easily imagine removing the doughnut from the space and seeing if another doughnut would fit inside it. In the same way, the set consisting of one object is different than the object itself, and we talk about them differently.

Having accepted this notion, it should be easy for you to imagine a set without *any* elements at all! In geometry, you imagined a point as having no length, width, or breadth at all, and in arithmetic you became familiar with the number zero which had no magnitude at all. In set theory, the *empty set,* or *zero set,* or *null set,* is the unique set which contains no elements at all. Notice that this set can be specified in many ways; in fact, sometimes we refer to it unknowingly. "The set of all even integers lying between 8 and 10" and "the set of cities having populations of 50,000,000 or more" are two descriptions of the same empty set. Since this set is unique, it is assigned the special symbol ϕ (the Greek letter "phi," pronounced "phee" by mathematicians). Notice that the number zero counts the members of the null set.

There's one other special set of great importance. It is called the *universal set,* and usually denoted by the symbol U. Everything that ever was, is, or ever will be is in this set. Sometimes, the universal set will be deliberately more narrowly defined for convenience. Thus one might define the set of all numbers, or the set of all people, or the set of all ledger accounts as the universal set *U*, if all subsequent discussion is to involve just members or subsets of that set. To avoid confusion the universal set is often defined so as to circumscribe the problem being considered, i.e., to separate out of the total universe those things that might conceivably have a bearing on the problem.

One last point about subsets: how many subsets can a set have? Surprisingly, this question can be very precisely answered. In the following list of exercises, one is already worked out for you. Work out the others, and see if you can decide how many subsets a set can have. The sequence of listing of the elements in a set, by the way, is inconsequential.

List all possible subsets of the following sets:

2. {*a*, 3, *R*}
    List: {*a*, 3, *R*}, {*a*, 3}, {*a*, *R*}, {3, *R*}, {*a*}, {3}, {*R*}, φ

    How many subsets? _____8_____

3. {5, *x*}
    List:

    How many subsets? _____

4. { +, −, ×, ÷ }
    List:

    How many subsets? _____

5. {*B*}
    List:

    How many subsets? _____

6. If a set has *n* elements, how many subsets can it have?

_____

From the exercise above you may have noted that the null set is considered to be a subset of every set. But why? To most of us the answer to this question is not obvious, so maybe the following explanation will help.

Given *A* = {*a*, *b*, *c*}, let us list in a special way all the possible ways in which the three elements in *A* can be combined.

For any particular subset it is possible for any one of the elements to be either *included* or *excluded* from the subset. Let us use a 1, then, to indicate the condition of an element's being included and 0 to indicate the condition of being excluded. We can now illustrate all possible combinations of the three elements of *A* as follows:

Element

a	b	c
1	1	1
1	0	1
1	1	0
1	0	0
0	1	1
0	1	0
0	0	1
0	0	0

Interpreting the table, the first entry (1, 1, 1) is equivalent to the subset $\{a, b, c\}$, the second entry (1, 0, 1) is equivalent to the subset $\{a, c\}$, etc. The last line in the listing above (0, 0, 0) represents the combination which has neither element a, nor b, nor c. And this, of course, is the null set, ϕ.

2.2 OPERATIONS WITH SETS: COMPLEMENTATION

In arithmetic, and later in elementary algebra, you learned the meaning of the operations of addition, subtraction, multiplication, and division, and others as well. The elements of your attention were numbers, and one wrote $2 + 3 = 5$ because the number denoted by the numeral "2" combined with the number denoted by the numeral "3" under the operation of addition denoted by the symbol "$+$" yielded the number denoted by the numeral "5." Operations in the alegbra of sets deal with sets and subsets in much the same way.

Just as in elementary algebra, where diagrams are helpful aids to understanding, the algebra of sets is blessed with its own special scheme for visualization. These drawings are termed *Venn diagrams*, after John Venn who suggested them in the late nineteenth century, in connection with his efforts to apply Boole's symbolic logic. In Venn's system, a circle or a rectangle or some other closed curve is used to represent a set in such a way that the area contained inside the curve stands for all elements which are in the set, and the area outside the curve stands for all elements which are not members of the set. Representing the universal set U by a large rectangle, one could draw the following figure:

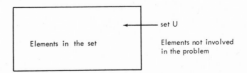

If we now describe a set *A* (sets are customarily denoted by upper case letters) as some subset of the universal set, then these elements are within the rectangle representing *U*. Suppose these elements of *A* are all drawn together:

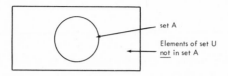

This diagram shows the separation of the universal set *U* into two subsets, the set *A* and the set of "not-*A*" elements. Since these two subsets together comprise the universal set, they are said to *partition* the universal set. If one of the two sets is called *A*, then the other set is called the *complement* of *A*, and is designated by the symbol $\overline{A}$. The bar ($^-$) on top of the letter designating a set indicates the operation of *complementation*, which is simply to find the complement of a set. The previous diagram can thus be labeled:

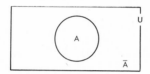

This operation of complementation is reminiscent of other operations in arithmetic and geometry. The reciprocal of a number is the number by which one multiplies the original to get the number 1. The complement of an angle is the angle one must add to the original to make a right angle. The complement of a set is the set one must "add" to the original to get the universal set.

 7. If we let the universal set *U* be the letters in the word "universal," what is the complement of each of the following sets:

$A = \{l, a, r, s, e, n\}$ $\overline{A} = $ _____

$B = \{s, i, n\}$ $\overline{B} = $ _____

$C = \{u, l, n, a, i, s, v, r, e\}$ $\overline{C} = $ _____

8. What does one call the complement of the empty set?

_____

9. What is the complement of the complement of the set $\{3, X, y\}$?

Sometimes it is necessary to indicate that an element "belongs to" (is a member of) a certain set. A symbol to denote this is in common use: "ε." To say that w is a letter of the alphabet, denote the set of all letters of the alphabet by the letter A, and write $w \ \varepsilon \ A$. This is read "the element w is a member of the set A." Note that this symbol is used to describe the relation between an element and a set, not between two elements nor between two sets. The symbol "$\notin$" is read "is not a member of," or "is not an element of."

 10. Translate the following mathematical statement into English: "$a \ \varepsilon \ A$ implies $a \notin \overline{A}$."

Is this statement true or false? Circle one: T   F

2.3 OPERATIONS WITH SETS: UNION AND INTERSECTION

One of the most important set operations, which corresponds roughly to addition in the algebra of numbers, is called *union*. It is denoted by the sign "$+$" connecting two sets, as in $A + B$, and is read as "A *union* B." The union of two sets is simply the set of elements which are in either one set, or the other, or in both. If set A consists of the integers from 3 to 10, and set B consists of the integers from 6 to 16, then the set $A + B$ consists of the integers 3 to 16. In the Venn diagram below, the two circles represent two different sets, and the shaded portion is then their union:

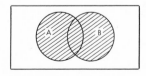

In shorthand, we can write: $x \ \varepsilon \ (A + B)$ implies either $x \ \varepsilon \ A$ or $x \ \varepsilon \ B$, or both. In plain English, if an element x is a member of the union of sets A and B, then it is a member of set A, set B, or of both. Note that if an element is a member of both sets, then it is a member just "one time" of the union. For example, the union of $\{w, x, y, z\}$ with $\{x, y\}$ is $\{w, x, y, z\}$, *not* $\{w, x, x, y, y, z\}$. Test your understanding of the notion of union in the following exercises:

11. Suppose the universal set U is the set of digits from 0 through 9, the set A is $\{0, 1, 2, 3\}$, and set B is $\{0, 1\}$. Perform the indicated operations by listing or describing the resultant set:

$\overline{A} + \phi =$ _____

$U + A =$ _____

$B + A =$ _____

$B + \phi =$ _____

$A + \overline{B} =$ _____

The next basic operation on sets is that of *intersection*, denoted by the symbol "·" similar to the dot used to indicate multiplication in elementary algebra.[1] Thus $A \cdot B$ is called "the intersection of sets A and B" or simply "A *intersect* B" and consists of all elements which are members of both A and B. Thus $x \; \varepsilon \; A \cdot B$ implies $x \; \varepsilon \; A$ *and* $x \; \varepsilon \; B$. The Venn diagram for this operation looks like this:

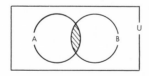

The shaded portion is the intersection of the two sets, since it contains all points (i.e., elements) which are inside (i.e., members of) both sets.

The elements of $A \cdot B$ are just the elements "common" to A and B, but sometimes two sets have no elements in common. The sets $\{0 \; 1, 2, 3\}$ and $\{-5, -3, -1\}$, for instance, have no common

---

[1] Many modern authors use the symbols $\cup$ and $\cap$ (called "cup" and "cap") instead of $+$ and $\cdot$ for union and intersection respectively: e.g., $A \; \cup \; B \equiv A + B$ and $A \; \cap \; B \equiv A \cdot B$. However, because the set operations of union and intersection are so closely analogous to the ordinary arithmetic operations of addition and multiplication, we prefer the "$+$" and "$\cdot$" notation. This notation tends to highlight similarities which, in turn, facilitates set manipulations.

elements. This does not mean that they do not *have* an intersection; they do, but it is *empty*. In other words, their intersection is the empty set ϕ. Two or more sets whose intersection is the empty set are said to be *disjoint*. Note that any set and its complement are always disjoint, by definition.

12. Suppose the universal set is all positive integers, set A is {5, 10, 15, 20} and set B is {5, 15, 25}. Perform the indicated operations by listing or describing the resultant set:

$U \cdot A =$ _____

$U \cdot B =$ _____

$A \cdot B =$ _____

$\phi \cdot A =$ _____

$A \cdot \overline{B} =$ _____

$A + (\overline{A} \cdot B) =$ _____

2.4 OTHER OPERATIONS WITH SETS

In set theory, it is possible to perform an operation similar to subtraction, in which one set is "taken away" from another. The symbol "−" is used to indicate the operation, but it is defined in terms of operations already discussed. The set $A - B$ consists of all elements which are members of set A but not also members of set B. But this is the same as those elements which are at the same time members of A and members of $\overline{B}$. Thus $A - B$ is the same as $A \cdot \overline{B}$. As a consequence, it is possible to avoid completely the use of the symbol "−" in set algebra, just as it is possible to use only plus signs with negative numbers in elementary algebra. In case it is convenient, though, the subtraction operation can be used.

The last basic operation in set theory was already defined earlier when subsets were discussed. When a set A is a subset of a set B, we say that A "is included in" B and write $A \subset B$. The symbol "⊂" is a little bit similar to the "less than" sign "<" of ordinary algebra, in that the "smaller" set is on the closed side of the "⊂" sign. It is important to distinguish between the signs "ε" and "⊂." The first is used to designate an element as a member of a set, while the second is used to designate a set as a subset of another set. If set A is {a, b, c, d}, then all of the following statements are true:

$a \; \varepsilon \; A,$ $b \; \varepsilon \; \{b, c\}$

$\{a\} \subset A,$ $\{b\} \subset \{a, b, c\} \subset A.$

In summary, the basic ideas in the algebra of sets are:

Universal set . . . . U
Empty set . . . . ϕ
Complement of set A . . . . $\overline{A}$
"Belongs to" . . . . ε
"Is a subset of" . . . . $\subset$
Union of sets A and B . . . . $A + B$
Intersection of sets A and B . . . . . . $A \cdot B$

If two sets A and B are shown on a Venn diagram, the various regions of the diagram may be labeled as shown:

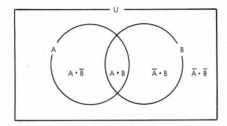

When three or more sets are considered together, the various subsets are designated in an exactly analogous way. For example, the intersection of three sets A, B, and C is designated $A \cdot B \cdot C$, as one would expect.

 13. In the following Venn diagram, some of the regions are already labeled. Label the others.

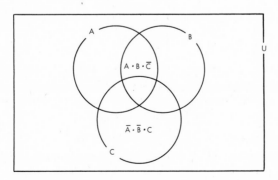

14. By looking at the completed diagram, state whether the following is a true statement:

$$(A \cdot \overline{B} \cdot \overline{C}) + (A \cdot B \cdot \overline{C}) = A \cdot \overline{C}$$

Before going on to some practical illustrations of the use of the theory outlined above, it should be pointed out that the equation of exercise 14 above can be manipulated directly without the Venn diagram. The various steps involved in reducing the left side of the equation to the right side are as follows:

By taking the common factors A and $\overline{C}$ from both terms on the left-hand

$$(A \cdot \overline{B} \cdot \overline{C}) + (A \cdot B \cdot \overline{C}) = (A \cdot \overline{C}) \cdot (\overline{B} + B)$$

But

$$(\overline{B} + B) = U$$

Therefore

$$(A \cdot \overline{B} \cdot \overline{C}) + (A \cdot B \cdot \overline{C}) = (A \cdot \overline{C}) \cdot (U).$$

But the intersect of any subset with U is just the subset itself.
Therefore

$$(A \cdot \overline{C}) \cdot (U) \qquad\qquad = A \cdot \overline{C}$$

or

$$(A \cdot \overline{B} \cdot \overline{C}) + (A \cdot B \cdot \overline{C}) = A \cdot \overline{C}.$$

As in the case with manipulation of elementary algebra, the use of well-defined rules makes it unnecessary for anyone to visualize mentally the results of each intermediate step while performing what are really very complicated reasoning problems. Boolean algebra, like the other kind, doesn't make things more difficult. In fact, it makes hard problems (in logic, for example) easy!

3.   Applying the Algebra of Sets

3.1   APPLICATION TO LOGIC PROBLEMS

We now have enough mathematical machinery available to solve most logic problems which might come along. Suppose we try the graphic approach on the problem given earlier in section 1.2. There were three rules governing the assignment of people to the Board of Directors, the Financial Committee, and the Appropriations Council. Let us designate these three sets of people as B, F, and A, respectively, and rewrite the rules in the language of Boolean algebra:

Rule (1): The Board of Directors appoints from among its members a Financial Committee.

Or: There are no members who are in F who are not in B

Or: $F \subset B$

Or: $F \cdot \overline{B} = \phi$.

Rule (2):No one shall serve on both the Board of Directors and Appropriations Council unless they are also on the Financial Committee.

Or: There are no members of both B and A not in F

Or: $(B \cdot A) \subset F$

Or: $B \cdot A \cdot \overline{F} = \phi$.

Rule (3): No member of the Appropriations Council shall be on the Financial Committee.

Or: There are no members in both A and F

Or: $A \cdot F = \phi$.

To visualize the combined effect of all three rules, we can draw a diagram and shade those subsets which are forbidden by each rule:

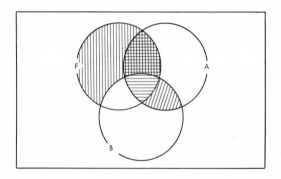

Forbidden by Rule 1, $F \cdot \overline{B} = \phi$: ||||||

Forbidden by Rule 2, $B \cdot A \cdot \overline{F} = \phi$: /////

Forbidden by Rule 3, $A \cdot F = \phi$: ≡

Now, *any* list of rules which prohibits these shaded areas (i.e., keeps members from belonging to the subsets represented by them) is equivalent (exactly) to the three rules stated. One such list is easily constructed:

(1) $F \cdot \overline{B} = \phi$

(2) $A \cdot B = \phi$

The Venn diagram for these two rules looks simpler but accomplishes the same objective.

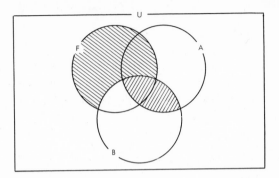

where Rule (1) is shaded $\backslash\backslash\backslash$ and Rule (2) shown as $/\!/\!/\!/\!/$. Clearly, the area shaded is just the same as that by the three rules, yet these are simpler. Translated into English again:

(1) $F \cdot \bar{B} = \phi$: No members shall be in F but not in B. Or: The Financial Committee shall be chosen from the Board of Directors.

(2) $A \cdot B = \phi$: No members shall be in A and also in B. Or: No member of the Board of Directors shall also serve on the Appropriations Council.

The use of Boolean algebra in this simple situation may appear to complicate matters unnecessarily. The purpose here was merely to demonstrate the application, not the power of Boolean algebra. As we shall see, however, this same approach can be applied in more complex situations in which the required results are not at all obvious.

3.2 APPLICATION TO ENUMERATION PROBLEMS

To illustrate the usefulness of Boolean algebra and especially the Venn diagram to a problem of a little different kind, consider the following example involving counting or enumeration:

A new recruit is given data on key-punch errors recorded during an audit of the data processing activity, and is asked to analyze and summarize the audit findings. The very first set of data was as follows:

L.A. Region Customer File Deck—Operator
Number 53102—Deck Punched 10/12/65.

Total cards in deck	1,507
Cards with error in an alphabetic field	21
Cards with error in a numeric field	9
Cards correctly punched	1,481

After a mental calculation ($1,481 + 9 + 21 = 1,511 \neq 1,507?$) the trainee sought out Operator 53102 and asked her to explain. With only a glance at the data (*without* Boolean algebra) she exclaimed, "Well, silly, obviously four cards had both kinds of errors!"

Operator 53102 was quite right; the answer should have been obvious even to a recruit. But not all such problems are so easy. Many are so intricate that they are nearly impossible to do without organizing the work usefully, either by using a Venn diagram or its equivalent. Suppose we show this simple key-punch error analysis in a Venn diagram, and then apply the same approach to a more difficult problem.

Let A = the set of cards with errors in the alphabetic fields, N be the set with errors in the numeric fields, and U be the universal set of all 1,507 cards. The following diagram enumerates the various subsets.

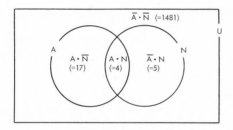

From the diagram, it is easy to see that set A has 21 members and set N has 9 members, just as the original data claimed, but that set $A + N$ does not have $21 + 9 = 30$ members, but only 26. Our diagram assigns to each area a number which represents the number of objects in the subset represented by that area. Now for a harder problem!

Suppose a survey of participation in an employee savings program in a particular organizational component revealed the following data: 9 male hourly, 5 hourly members, 9 male salaried, 7 hourly nonmembers, 14 members, 6 male members, 7 female nonmembers, and 2 male salaried members.

How many people are in the component altogether? Better yet, how many are in *each* of the possible classes? To solve this problem, define the three classes:

Members / Nonmembers . . . . $(A / \overline{A})$
Salaried / Nonsalaried (hourly) . . . . . $(B / \overline{B})$
Male / Nonmale (female) . . . . $(C / \overline{C})$

The Venn diagram, with all areas labeled, is as follows:

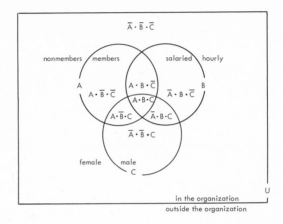

By inspection of the Venn diagram, it is now possible to express the original data in equation form as follows:

(1) Male hourly: $\qquad 9 = A \cdot \overline{B} \cdot C + \overline{A} \cdot \overline{B} \cdot C$

(2) Hourly members: $\qquad 5 = A \cdot \overline{B} \cdot C + A \cdot \overline{B} \cdot \overline{C}$

(3) Male salaried: $\qquad 9 = A \cdot B \cdot C + \overline{A} \cdot B \cdot C$

(4) Hourly nonmembers: $\qquad 7 = \overline{A} \cdot \overline{B} \cdot C + \overline{A} \cdot \overline{B} \cdot \overline{C}$

(5) Members: $\qquad 14 = A \cdot B \cdot C + A \cdot B \cdot \overline{C} + A \cdot \overline{B} \cdot C + A \cdot \overline{B} \cdot \overline{C}$

(6) Male members: $\qquad 6 = A \cdot B \cdot C + A \cdot \overline{B} \cdot C$

(7) Female nonmembers: $\qquad 7 = \overline{A} \cdot B \cdot \overline{C} + \overline{A} \cdot \overline{B} \cdot \overline{C}$

(8) Male salaried members: $\quad 2 = A \cdot B \cdot C$

The problem is solved, at least in theory, for the above are eight equations in eight unknown quantities, which can readily be solved for the eight variables. This is easier than it looks, for only one, two, or four variables appear together in a single equation. One method of solution is to proceed stepwise as follows:

eq. (3) $\qquad\qquad A \cdot B \cdot C + \overline{A} \cdot B \cdot C = 9$

eq. (8) $\qquad\qquad A \cdot B \cdot C \qquad\qquad = 2$

subtract to get eq. (9): $\qquad\qquad \overline{A} \cdot B \cdot C = 7$

eq. (6) $\qquad\qquad A \cdot B \cdot C + A \cdot \overline{B} \cdot C = 6$

eq. (8) $\qquad\qquad A \cdot B \cdot C \qquad\qquad = 2$

subtract to get eq. (10): $\qquad\qquad A \cdot \overline{B} \cdot C = 4$

eq. (1) $A \cdot \overline{B} \cdot C + \overline{A} \cdot \overline{B} \cdot C = 9$

eq. (10) $A \cdot \overline{B} \cdot C \phantom{+ \overline{A} \cdot \overline{B} \cdot C} = 4$

subtract to get eq. (11): $\overline{A} \cdot \overline{B} \cdot C = 5$

(and so forth)

As the count in each subset in the diagram is identified by the method shown above, it simplifies matters by adding the count to the appropriate area of the Venn diagram. The subsets enumerated thus far are shown by the figures in the circles below:

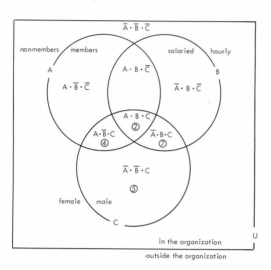

At this point it is almost possible to do the remaining work in one's head using just the diagram and the original data. For instance, determining that there were 4 male hourly members ($A \cdot \overline{B} \cdot C = 4$) and knowing from the original data that there were 5 hourly members leads to the conclusion that one hourly member must be female ($A \cdot \overline{B} \cdot \overline{C} = 1$). Entering this figure on the Venn diagram leads to the conclusion that there must be 7 female salaried members ($A \cdot B \cdot \overline{C} = 7$), since from the original data there were 14 members in total, 7 of which we have already accounted for. In similar fashion, see if you can determine the number of people comprising the subsets $\overline{A} \cdot \overline{B} \cdot \overline{C}$ and $\overline{A} \cdot B \cdot \overline{C}$. You can check your results on the diagram on the following page. (The arrows on the diagram indicate one possible way of proceeding for all subsets.)

From this Venn diagram, it is now possible to answer all enumeration questions. There were 33 employees in the organization, 18

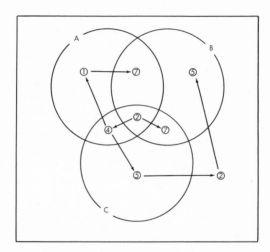

males and 15 females, 21 salaried and 12 hourly, 14 savings program members and 19 nonmembers, 12 female salaried employees (can you verify this number from the diagram?), and so on for any subset one cares to name.

All enumeration problems are similar in principle. Very large ones, such as are encountered in the U.S. Census and other elaborate studies involving many different ways of classifying a set of objects, use high-speed computers for all the intricate calculations that are involved. Of course, many of the basic ideas behind this type of problem also come up in designing computer systems involving large files with many cross-classified items. Structure tables, list-processing programing languages, and the design of computer components themselves are based on these principles from the theory of sets.

Practice Problem

In a certain Company, the eligibility rules covering monthly payments to pensioners are as follows:

  a. Pensioners aged 70 or more receive Ordinary Pensions.
  b. Ordinary pensioners retired before January 1, 1956, receive, in addition to their Ordinary Pensions, a Past Service Adjustment Payment.
  c. Pensioners retired on or after January 1, 1956 with 20 or more years

of accredited service receive, in addition to other pension payments, a Long Service Supplemental Payment.

d. Pensioners aged less than 70 receive Reduced Pensions, except that such pensioners retired before January 1, 1956, with 20 or more years of accredited service, receive, in addition to the Reduced Pension, a Past Service Adjustment Payment.

On the basis of this information, answer the following questions regarding the plan:

1. A man who retired on September 30, 1961, at the age of 62, after 29 years of accredited service, would be eligible for what payments during 1964?

   Answer: _____   _____

   _____

2. A man who now receives a Reduced Pension and Past Service Adjustment Payment can expect a change in benefits at some future date. What are the terms of the pension he will eventually become eligible for?

   Answer: _____

   _____

(*Hint:* Mark a Venn diagram with symbols such as *OP* for Ordinary Pension, *PSAP* for Past Service Adjustment Payment, etc. The three sets to consider are (1) Pensioners aged 70 or more, (2) Pensioners with 20 or more years of service, and (3) Pensioners retired before January 1, 1956. The universal set is, of course, the set of all pensioners.)

A check of the pension plan records revealed the following statistical information concerning the 1,770 pensioners on the Company's roles:

752 pensioners are retired with 20 or more years of service

293 pensioners, of the 752 retired with 20 or more years of service, are under 70 years of age

896 pensioners were retired before January 1, 1956

1,216 pensioners are drawing Ordinary Pensions

810 pensioners are drawing Past Service Adjustment Payments

620 pensioners are drawing both Ordinary Pensions and Past Service Adjustment Payments

402 pensioners are drawing Long Service Supplemental Payments

On the basis of this data, answer the following questions:

1. How many pensioners retired before January 1, 1956, with less than 20 years service?

                              Answer _____

2. How many pensioners are drawing Ordinary Pensions only?

                              Answer _____

3. How many of the pensioners that retired since January 1, 1956 are under 70 and have less than 20 years service?

                              Answer _____

(*Hint:* On the Venn diagram, label each area with the number of pensioners in the set represented by the area.)

General Index

A

Absolute value, 16
Accuracy of data, 28–30
Algebra
  Boolean, 200–202
  elementary, 202
  and the man in the street, 73–76
  of matrices, 172–98
  of sets, 172, 199–220
  review of, 73–112
  rules, 79–88
Analytic geometry, 144, 173
Antilog, 108
Arithmetic mean, 48–54
Array, 36
Association
  closeness, 117
  degree of, 116–17
  and estimating, 115–16
  nature, 116–17
Automobile production, 27
Averages
  definitions, 47–51
  properties of, 51–54
Average velocity, 148–50
Axioms, 5

B

Base of logarithms, 84, 105
Bimodal, 50
Binomial, 86
Bivariate data
  defined, 34
  example of, 113–15
  organizing, 43–45
Boolean algebra, 200–202
Boole, George, 200

C

Calculus
  differential, 144–65
  integral, 165–70
Central tendency, 48
Change, rate of, 145–48
Characteristic of logarithm, 107
Class interval, 36–37, 41
Classification of variables, 32–34
Closeness of fit, 119
Coefficient
  of correlation, 128, 133–35
  of determination, 128, 133–35
  of variation, 70

Coleridge, Samuel Taylor, 76
Column vector, 176–77
Common logarithms; *see also*
  Logarithms
  tables, 103–4
Common nouns, 9
Complement of a set, 206–8
Complementation, 202, 206–8
Components of a matrix, 177
Conditional
  equation, 90
  inequality, 97
Constant, 7–9
Continuous variable, 32–34
Coordinate axes, 14
Correlation
  coefficient of, 133–35
  measuring, 128–32
  perfect, 131, 133
Critical path, 51
Cross-classification, 34, 115
Cumulative
  frequency distribution, 39–40
  percentage frequency distribution,
    40–42
Curve
  fitting, 135–43
  forms, 140–42
  normal, 68–69
Curvilinear relationship, 117

D

Data quality, 28–30
Decision tree, 198
Degree
  of association, 116–17, 119
  of correlation, 134
  of relationship, 128
Delta method, 155–58
Dependent variable, 117
Derivative
  definition, 148–52
  equal to zero, 161–62
  graphic interpretation, 152–56
  max and min problems, 160–65
  rules for finding, 156–60
  of a sum, 158–59
Descartes, 144, 173
Determination, coefficient of, 128,
  133–35
Deviations, 53, 129–30
Differential calculus, 148, 151
Dimension of matrix, 184

This book has been set in 11 and 10 point Caledonia, leaded 2 points. Chapter numbers are in 9 point Futura Demi caps and 18 point Tempo Heavy Bold; chapter titles are in 18 point Tempo Bold italics. The size of the type page is 27 by 46½ picas.